FREDERICK LINCOLN FULLER

MY HALF CENTURY
AS AN
INVENTOR

By

FREDERICK L. FULLER

To the memory of Rebecca Hamilton Bell Fuller, whose dear companionship in marriage was my comfort and blessing for the fifty-six years from 1881 to 1937, and who during her long, useful and cheerful life was in every sense my guardian angel, this book is affectionately dedicated.

FOREWORD

Every generation produces a certain number of individuals whose fortunate lot it is to contribute to the general good of mankind. The works of many of these men and women have been in the field of science and invention, which have been responsible for more progress in the last hundred and fifty years than had been made in all the preceding centuries of human history.

My friend Frederick Lincoln Fuller is a member of that select company of men upon whom Providence has conferred inquiring minds and the additional boon of practicality. From his early boyhood Mr. Fuller has viewed life in terms of "doing things better". This has meant doing them more easily. His practical mind has helped him patent nearly a hundred inventions which have been incorporated into machines which bring peace of mind through elimination of drudgery.

His life, like that of a majority of great inventors and scientists, has been one of simplicity as well as of service. His personality has endeared him to an immediate circle of friends which will be widened to include, I am sure, every reader of this story of his life. He gives me credit for having inspired this narrative of a useful career, and I am very glad to have had a part in making it possible for others to get a glimpse at the human side of a truly great inventor.

THOS. J. WATSON.

CHAPTER I

Almost at the moment—noon of April 11, 1861—that the Confederate command in Charleston, S. C., ordered the Union garrison to evacuate Fort Sumter, I was born. In the city of my birth—charming and historic Norwich, Conn.—I spent my youth and early manhood. Too young to have had any interest in the war between the states, I was thrown on my own resources as the result of its aftermath, the panic of '73.

For sixty-two years I have been dependent for my livelihood upon my own efforts, and in reviewing these interesting decades I have finally arrived at the conclusion that my destiny was shaped by kindly hands. For I was blessed with an active and inquiring mind, and if my father had not lost his paper mill in the panic I might have had no more excitement in my life than comes to the average heir to a business who is expected to continue it whether or not that is where his fancy lies.

Instead, I have had the rare privilege of sharpening my wits on a continuous succession of problems demanding solution. I have learned the value of patient and painstaking effort and the folly of listening to those whose first reaction to new ideas is that "it can't be done." I have learned to listen, to discuss, to observe, to study and to think things through. The short and easy road to the mastery of all these lessons was denied me. My classroom education stopped abruptly in my early teens, and ever since then I have had to acquire my learning in the hard but excellent school of practical experience. After more than sixty years of this, one of the greatest and most durable satisfactions of my life lies in the realization that I still have lessons to learn, problems to solve—and that as long as I live this will continue to be the case.

In my early twenties I discovered the path leading to the United States Patent Office in Washington, and I have kept my feet upon it constantly down to the present day. For as many years as I am destined to remain on earth I expect to follow it.

It is a source of great satisfaction to me that as the result of inventions I have had the good fortune to perfect, there are in every important city in the world—and in thousands of villages so unimportant that they are unheard of at more than a score or so of miles—machines which are expediting the transactions of commerce and industry, finance and government institutions, and relieving human brains of humdrum, repetitious tasks that fall into the general classification of drudgery.

In response to the urging of my long-time friend Thomas J. Watson, I have undertaken the preparation of this simple story of my life. My first association with Mr. Watson was in Dayton, O., and we worked together for many years in those early days. Later, as the story will tell, we resumed this very close relationship. I am indebted to Mr. Watson for many kindnesses. Chief among them, I think, was his insistence ten years ago that I was too young to retire. Already suspicious, after a couple of years of long anticipated leisure, that the joys of retirement had been more in its anticipation than in its realization, I listened to Mr. Watson and, at the age of 66, undertook a career in an entirely new field of activity. Due to his advice the last ten years have been among the happiest and most productive of my life.

When I first met Mr. Watson, nearly thirty years ago, he was a young, resourceful, enthusiastic and successful sales executive. I still find him resourceful, enthusiastic and successful—and if it is true that youth lies in the continuing activity of the mind, a younger man than he was when first we met.

So I have allowed him to persuade me that the events of such a life as mine can be woven into a story that will interest the young who are just starting life, the old who are approaching its end, and those who are no longer young and not yet old. To all of these I extend my greetings.

CHAPTER II

When I was a youngster, boys had to furnish their own amusements. We had no automobiles to ride in or airplanes to aspire to. Motion pictures were unheard of. "Chores" of one sort or another were the common lot of the sons of well-to-do and poor families. It was the general belief that a boy must learn early in life to accept responsibility. The kitchen woodpile, the lawn mower, the house heating arrangements and similar stints always fell on young shoulders.

But we had plenty of fun. I imagine I had more than most boys because I had a grandfather named Owen Stead. My mother's father. She had been Lucy May Stead when she married my father, Charles C. Fuller. My grandfather was the kindest, most sympathetic and understanding man I have ever known, and from him I inherited the love of machinery and its workings which, after much youthful groping about, was to set me finally upon the path of mechanical invention.

Having retired from the superintendency of one of the departments of the large cotton mill in Norwich, he was engaged in broom manufacture when I grew large enough to frequent his shop. It must have been when I was about six years old that he rigged up a scroll saw for me—and I had a grand time making banjos and clocks and jigsaw ornaments for furniture. Grandfather always had been a great hand for experiments—both at the cotton mill and in his own shop he invented many better ways to perform familiar tasks. I remember still the patience with which he used to explain these things to me. I cherished the belief that he was the greatest man in the world and it was my greatest hope that I could grow up to be like him. I was so ambitious to learn that when I was only ten or eleven years old I had mastered the trick of making simple turnings on a small wood lathe.

Grandfather Stead was a great lover of children and they flocked around him like bees around a flower bed. I remember that there were about eight boys among his grandchildren, all about the same age. Whenever any of the numerous family reunions brought us all together every boy would clamor for the privilege of sleeping with grandfather. Two and sometimes even three of us would win, and after we were all in bed the old gentleman would tell us the most exciting bear stories and other yarns based on his own boyhood experiences. He would grow tired long before we did, and every now and then he would go to sleep right in the middle of a sentence. But when we would nudge him awake he would go right on with the sentence as if he hadn't been asleep at all. Which would keep up until all of us were too sleepy for any more stories.

When I was nearly through high school my father lost his mill. The severity of this unexpected business calamity broke his health, and he died at the age of 48, after several years of illness. I have always felt that heartbreak over the collapse of all his plans for his family was the true cause of his demise.

I was only 14 years old when my father's breakdown threw our family with unbelievable abruptness into an entirely new way of life. My mother took in boarders, my sister found work as a school teacher, and I was obliged to hunt a job that would enable me to contribute my bit toward the support of all of us.

A family friend was Robert A. France, who was assistant treasurer of the Chelsea Paper Mills in Norwich. He had charge of the office, and he put me to work as office boy. In addition to other duties, I had to keep the time of the nineteen workmen in the mill. As I grew more familiar with the work I was allowed to figure the costs of new work and repairs. For a number of years my whole world revolved about that paper mill. We made book paper of fine grade. Our poorest paper—and it was much

My grandfather, Owen Stead, *the kindest man I have ever known*

better than papers used for similar purposes today—was made for Harper's Weekly. I can still remember the size—33 x 46 inches, seventy-five pounds to the ream. All our paper was made from the best grade of rags. We had five machines and a daily output of ten tons of paper.

My wages when I started in the paper mill office were $5.00 a week. After what I thought was too long a time without an increase, I went into the mill to learn paper making, and immediately earned $9.00 a week. A dollar went much farther then than it does today and this was pretty good pay for a youngster, in addition to which I was learning every phase of the paper making trade. The men in the mill were nice chaps and I enjoyed my work very much.

I have often wondered how I missed being a railroad man, for at this period of my life I was almost more interested in railroads than I was in my own work. The Norwich and Worcester Railroad had its southern terminal in our town, and I was greatly interested in the engines. In all there were twenty-one of these locomotives, and I knew every one of them—not only by number but by the sounds of their bells and whistles. I could tell a mile away which one was coming into town. I also knew most of the engineers and firemen. This personal acquaintance with the men who ran the locomotives almost cost me my life.

Part of my job each day was to ride the train that carried our paper output down to Norwich Landing, a few miles from the mill, when I would see it on board the steamer and take the captain's receipt for it. Several of the engineers would take me into their cabs for the ride down the line. I would sit on the fireman's seat, ringing the bell while he shovelled coal into the firebox. Once, and it was about my last ride in an engine cab, my engineer friend beckoned me to come over to his side of the cab. He wanted to tell me something. I had scarcely left the fireman's seat when the connecting rod on the left side of the engine broke and began to thrust into the cab, right where I had been sitting! The engine didn't upset, but we had a rough ride for a few yards and I would have been chopped to mince-meat but for the merest chance.

That experience, and one more, just about finished my desire to ride on engines. This time it was a bit of practical economy that brought me one of the thrills of my life.

Competition between the railroads that ran between New York and Boston was so keen that the fare was cut to one dollar each way. It still cost three dollars to ride from Norwich to Boston—three times as much for a ride about half as long. That difference was important to a young man in my circumstances, and on the rare occasions when I had to go to Boston I resorted to a scheme that I had figured out to cut my traveling costs. Eight miles from Norwich there was a station on the main line called Allen's Point, and I would cover that distance on a work train that ran down from Norwich and came back late at night. Then I would buy a dollar ticket, for they charged the same fare from all intermediate stations, and my round trip expense would be just one third what it would have been going direct from Norwich, as it didn't cost me anything to ride on the work train, which was not supposed to carry passengers.

This always worked well until one night when an official of the road happened to be at Allen's Point and forbade me to ride the work train back home. I had always ridden in the engine cab, and on this occasion the engineer said he would slow down as he left the yards, so that I could hop onto the cowcatcher for the eight mile ride.

"Just perch up under the headlight", he said. "No one will know you are there and I'll get you to Norwich in jig time. I'll slow down as we approach the yards there and you can hop off all right."

I had no misgivings as I hopped onto that cowcatcher and climbed up to my perch under the headlight. But I had hardly settled down when my friend at the throttle threw it wide open and we began to split the wind at a rate that plastered me against the engine as if I had been cast there when the front was made in the foundry. I couldn't even shut my eyes. The wind kept my eyelids glued back. That old locomotive, with a clear track ahead, made a new speed record, and when it slowed down for the Norwich yards I had just enough strength left to hop off safely. I was pretty mad and went down to the roundhouse, but the laugh the engineer and fireman gave me when I appeared made me see the funny side of it and I contented myself with the resolution that I wouldn't ride on any more cowcatchers. I have kept that resolution without difficulty.

We depended on simple things for our amusements. One of the great sports in Norwich was boating. The city was at the junction of the Shetucket and the Yantic rivers, where they united to form the River Thames, and we used to manage to see the Yale-Harvard boat races at New London every year. We boys were all steamed up about rowing. One summer I got some of my chums to work with me, and we built a real racing shell. An eight oared shell, more than thirty feet long. We pooled our savings to buy, in New London, regular racing oars. They were fourteen feet long with spoon blades; the same sort of oars used by the college crews.

We had lots of fun designing and building that shell, but we never were able to have a race. We rowed plenty of practice spins, of course, but these were a bit cramped. The only place we could row was in the power canal, which took water out of the Shetucket and carried it through the Norwich mill district, returning it to the river lower down. As this canal was only fifty feet wide, and the spread of our midship oars was more than thirty feet, there was no room for any boat to race us, even if there had been another racing boat there. We would practice our sprints, and each time we came to an end of the canal we would all have to

Our homestead in Norwich. Insets at top, my father and mother. Lower insets are my wife and myself

pile out and carry the shell up on the canal bank to turn it around. It was too long to turn in the water. I remember that when the shell broke in two as we were rowing one day, and we all had to swim ashore, we agreed that it was too bad. But nothing was said about rebuilding it. We had had our fun.

After I had been working in the paper office and mill about four years I met a girl. Her full name was Rebecca Hamilton Bell, and her friends called her Becky. She was only fourteen years old, and I was eighteen. Before that I had never had much to do with girls, and as soon as I met Becky I felt that I never would have much to do with any of them except her. For the next two years I saw her whenever I could and we got to be better and better friends. About half of my spare time was spent writing down sums to prove that $9.00 a week was enough for two people to live on. As soon as I was convinced of this important truth it was up to me to convince Becky. She had been graduated from High School and was preparing to enter the Norwich Academy, but I succeeded in proving to her that instead she would do better to marry me. Better for me, I meant, and that was the way it turned out.

Our marriage in 1881 was the start of a partnership that lasted for fifty-six years. When we began our married life we knew that we were no different from other couples—that we would have occasional spats and misunderstandings. So we entered into a compact that never would we go to bed, at the end of however troubled a day, without making up our differences. We lived up to that easily—for we had fewer quarrels than most couples I have known—and when Mrs. Fuller passed away in the summer of 1937 I think she was sustained to the end by the knowledge that she had contributed more than a full share to a happy and successful marriage.

Soon after our wedding I decided that the opportunities in the paper business were too limited to insure a comfortable future.

In Norwich I had won a reputation for steadiness, so when I applied for a job I had heard was open at the Norwich brass foundry I was hired at once. The pay envelope continued to contain $9.00 weekly, but I was learning a trade that would pay me $3.00 a day eventually, so it seemed to be a wise move. The job, however, lasted only six months. The gases from the melting brass were too much for my health. Our doctor said if I didn't walk out of there immediately they might carry me out soon—and so I was obliged to make another change. For the next six months I ran a cloth stretching machine at the Norwich Bleachery, and finally was obliged to give up this job also, as it was too confining.

It seems strange to me now to remember that I was so thin in those days that everybody thought I had tuberculosis. I remember the conviction of the tailor who made my clothes that I would die of consumption before I was twenty-one years old.

About this time I narrowly missed fulfilling the gloomy expectations of the tailor, although not by the tuberculosis route. It happened through my interest in rifle shooting, which was a popular sport in Norwich. The international matches at Creedmoor in England were as exciting and interesting to us as world series baseball games are today. Our interest didn't end with reading about other men shooting; we went into target practice ourselves. The roof of our barn was our shooting stand, and a field that ran back about a quarter of a mile, into a steep hill, was an ideal rifle range. Our target was an old piano box, and we blazed away at it from every shooting position included in the Creedmoor competition. I attempted a shot that required me to lie on my back with my feet toward the target. I was too tall for the short rifle I was using, and the flash from the muzzle set my trousers afire. The bullet just grazed my shoe and so I gave up shooting for fear I would meet with a more serious and possibly fatal accident. Before my marriage I would have kept right on, but I was too conscious of my responsibilities to take needless chances.

After working six months in the bleachery I went back to the paper business. For a few months I was employed in Hubbard's Mill and then went back to the Chelsea. But I still felt the paper business offered too little to hold me permanently.

There was a man living in Norwich who was a true craftsman. His name was William H. Page. He had a very successful business in the manufacture of wood type—block type cut from blocks of highly polished maple—and also wood cuts which were engraved on box wood. Mr. Page also was an inventor. He designed the Page Steam Boiler and made the patterns himself from which the metal moulds were made. His boiler factory occupied the ground floor and his type factory the upper floor of his building. It was a distinction to be on his payroll, as he was very particular about the men he hired. So I was quite flattered to have my application for a job in the boiler shop acted upon favorably, and left the paper mill for the last time to run a drill press on Page boilers.

While I was working at the Page shop I had a distressing accident that not only maimed me permanently but also taught me a lesson—not to make snap judgments on serious things. I was sawing out the parts for a wooden tool box for my own use. By the way, I still have that box, and use it. It has gone with me in all my moves over more than half a century and I have become quite attached to it. Well, on the day I was making it I had sawed some of the parts on a power saw. Something distracted my attention from the work, and when I turned to the saw again I started to pick up one of the pieces without realizing that I had not shut off the saw.

Most people have a definite theory as to what will happen if a finger comes into contact with a revolving saw. My own knowledge is based on practice rather than theory, for my fingers did just that. In a fraction of a second the saw had taken off the ball of my left thumb, broken and mangled the index finger and severely bruised the middle finger. The boys at the mill rigged up a rude tourniquet which stopped the bleeding, and rushed me to the town doctor. The practice of medicine and surgery in those days lacked most of the refinements and sanitary conveniences that are familiar to all of us today. The doctor looked at my hand and said:

"Which do you want to have, a stiff finger, or a short one?"

When I said I would prefer a short one he reached into his instrument case and promptly amputated my left index finger just below the large knuckle.

He then bound up my hand, after repairing the ball of the thumb as best he could, and in a couple of weeks I was back at work. I made some leather finger cots to cover the stump of my finger until it should heal completely, and in a short time the stiffness wore out of the hand. But even today, the stump of that finger is sensitive and I have given it many a hard bump that has made me regret that I did not elect to leave it on my hand, even if it would have been stiff and awkward.

We carried the mail! In this picture of the first Norwich carriers, the author is fourth from left

CHAPTER III

Although I enjoyed my work in the Page boiler plant, my health showed no improvement. The doctors said I would have to have out door work before I could expect to become robust. And it was at this time that an opportunity presented itself for a job that was to keep me out of doors, in sun and rain, heat and cold, up hill and down dale, for more than two years. I was one of the first five men to don the uniform of mail carrier in Norwich.

The city had just reached the status of carrier delivery of mail, and the postmaster, George Bidwell, was organizing his staff. There were no civil service examinations in those days and Mr. Bidwell had been in the Shetucket Cloth Mills where he had worked under my grandfather. So it was a simple matter for grandfather's influence to get me the post of carrier for my district. My route was twenty-one miles long, or at any rate I traveled that distance every day in covering it. Before a change in the national administration, and the advent of a Democratic postmaster, threw me out of this job, I walked more than 16,000 miles with a mail carrier's sack over my shoulder. That experience not only restored me to robust health. It started me on my life work as an inventor.

In addition to plenty of walking, the mail job kept me at work for long hours. My working day began at 6:30 o'clock in the morning, and lasted until 8:30 in the evening. But in this fourteen hour stretch there were three long intervals for breakfast, dinner and supper. My route included the several mills in that part of Norwich known as Greenville, and my last stop in the evening collection trip was at the Norwich Bleachery, where I would wait while the superintendent, Albert Tillinghast, finished signing the mail. I became well acquainted with him and he formed the habit of talking to me about developments in the bleachery, such as new machinery and improved methods. One evening, with considerable pride, he showed me the new Slocum Time Recording System which had been installed to keep the time of the men.

This contraption consisted of a circular receptacle divided into pockets which were moved under a chute by a clock. At certain hours different pockets would be under the chute, the workmen would drop their checks in the top of the chute and the timekeeper was supposed to be able to tell when they had started and when they had quit by the pockets in which he found their checks. It was all right if the timekeeper didn't mix up the checks, but this seemed to me to be almost impossible. We spent lots of time discussing this device. Mr. Tillinghast thought it was a wonder and tried every argument he could think of to make me agree. Our discussions went on for a week or more; he extolling the system, I ridiculing it. Finally he lost his patience and asked me:

"Do you think you could make a better time recorder than that?"

"I don't think I could," I replied. "I know I could."

"Well," he said, "as soon as you can convince me of that I will get together with some of my friends in Providence and we will back you on putting it on the market. But don't forget, you'll have to prove to me that it is a better time recorder than this one."

My confidence that I could better the old Slocum Time Recorder was based in part upon my experience in the paper mill, where the keeping of the time of the men had been a tedious chore. I had had some vague ideas of a machine to do this work before I ever saw the Slocum, but nothing before had pinned me down to the necessity of working them out. Now I was up against a real chore. I knew very little about draughtmanship. I never had had a drawing lesson. As a boy I had made banjos and clocks on my scroll saw, and later had built a few boats, but about all that was in favor of my working out my time recorder was that I had a definite idea and was handy with tools.

It was a tough grind. I found out that there was a lot of difference between having an idea and working it out, first on paper, and then in a working model. Here my grandfather, Owen Stead, gave me the encouragement and assistance that kept me plugging away.

"Don't be discouraged, Fred," he would say in his kindly way. "If you know where you're going and keep at it, you'll get there all right."

Grandfather not only gave me his moral support, but frequently made suggestions based on his instinctive knowledge of mechanics and his years of practical experience, that were of tremendous value. And finally I had a working model of the machine on which I got my first patent, No. 379,865.

But while I was working on this model I lost my job in the post office. Not for inattention to my duties. My experimental work was all done in the ten hours daily I had to myself, away from my job. The cause of my discharge was political. I had been appointed at the end of President Arthur's term, and after the election of Grover Cleveland we knew that it was only a question of time before we would have as postmaster a Democrat, who would appoint an entirely new set of carriers. I served long enough after Cleveland's inauguration, however, to deliver to members of the Hyde family in Norwich, pieces of the wedding cake served at his marriage to their kinswoman, Miss Frances Folsom, in the White House on June 2, 1886. These souvenirs came through in the mail and were handled with the utmost care.

Eventually the political steam roller flattened out my job and then I had nothing to do but complete my time recorder model. I was mighty proud when Mr. Tillinghast agreed that my time recorder was far ahead of the Slocum or of anything else of the kind that he had imagined. Of course when I refer to the model I completed in Norwich I must make it clear that this really was more a series of sketches worked out in metal than a model as the term is understood in engineering and shop practice. I had gone far enough, however, to convince Mr. Tillinghast, and he kept his word and sent me to Providence, where his brother, Allen Tillinghast, and a number of other men provided me with money and a place where I could make a real model.

When my work had progressed to the point where I was ready to file my first patent application, I had the assistance of Frank H. Allen as patent attorney. There was a lot of work connected with the preparation of the application. This was all new and strange to me, but the necessity for each special form of verbiage was explained to me as we went along, and I do not think I had ever had as great a thrill, up to that time, as I got when the application was finished, signed, attested and witnessed and actually placed in the mail. For a while I watched the returning mail with feverish eagerness, although I knew that many months must elapse before I would learn whether my application had resulted in the issuance of a patent. In fact, just about a year after I sent in that first application I sent in another, claiming certain improvements on the original design, and it was nearly three months after the dispatch of the latter application before the patent was issued on the first one. The exact dates were January 8, 1887, for the first application; January 16, 1888, for the second, and March 20, 1888, for the issuance of the first patent.

My first working model of a time recorder was completed in Providence. It was rather small and crude. The Tillinghasts wanted a more complete machine, so I suggested that I be sent to Waterbury, Conn., to carry on my work. This city was the national center of manufacture of metal models.

In those days most models were constructed in brass. This was the easiest metal to work, and facilities in Waterbury were unexcelled. Sheet steel as we know it today did not exist. So off to Waterbury I went—and here I not only made a bigger and better time recorder model but also carried on my first experiments with cash registers.

Albert Tillinghast died while I was working on my time recorder model in Waterbury. This affected me deeply, as he was a good friend, and the first man who had had enough confidence in my ability to back me in more important work than carrying mail or learning to make paper. His death not only grieved me very much, but proved to be the introduction to my next step in the field of inventions. As he had been the moving spirit in the formation of the company organized to manufacture my time recorder, the men associated with him lost interest in it after his death, and the ambitious plans which had been formulated to make and market my time recorder were discarded.

I have always regretted this, for I still feel that my time recorder was the equal of any then made, and if we had kept on with it, it would have been subject to the natural changes demanded by increased acceptance and changing conditions, and might even now be a leader in the important field of employee time recording.

The company that had been formed to market it bore the name of the Argus Time Recorder Company.

The death of Mr. Tillinghast and the abandonment of the Argus Company left me once more out of a job, but again my period of unemployment was so brief as to be hardly noticeable. I had done my work on the time recorder model in the shop of the Specialty Manufacturing Company, owned by the Griswold family. Mr. Griswold and his two sons, Arthur and George, were actively engaged in the shop work, which included the manufacture to order of models for many sorts of devices and appliances. There was a cordiality in the atmosphere of this shop which made it an unusually pleasant place to work, and I had become especially friendly with young George Griswold. He was said to be the handsomest man in Waterbury and while he was a conscientious worker at the bench I know now that he was miscast in that role. He was a born salesman.

All the Griswolds shared my disappointment at the abandonment of the Argus enterprise. We had many talks about my future plans, which to say the least were indefinite. I had begun to wonder if it was going to be my lot in life to be passed around from one indifferent job to another, never getting anywhere, when the Griswolds made me a proposition that revived my fallen spirits and filled me with even greater enthusiasm than I had felt when working on my own time recorder. It was made plain to me that they wanted me to work for them not because they liked me, but because they thought I had talent in model making and designing, and when they said they would pay me a salary of $25.00 every week I felt that I was indeed on the way to a worthwhile success. Only a couple of years before I had been carrying the mail for $50.00 a month, out of which I had to buy my own uniforms. Here I was, in Waterbury, with more than twice as much salary for much more congenial work. No wonder I threw out my chest and resolved to prove to the Griswolds that they had made no mistake.

This was in 1888. I had never seen a cash register. They were not widely known, and only a few merchants had them. In fact, it might be said that the cash register at that time was as rare in New England as the lion, of which there were only two or three in zoological parks.

But there was a model of a cash register in the Griswold factory. It was being made for some inventor. I was assigned to work on parts of the model, and lost no opportunity to study the machine as a whole, to see how well it would serve the purpose for which it was intended. I finally came to the conclusion that there were many ways in which a better cash register could be made, and one day I made bold to say as much to Mr. Griswold.

It seems strange to think that his reply to this observation was in the same words that Mr. Tillinghast had used when I had made fun of his Slocum Time Recorder.

"Do you think you can make a better one?" he asked.

And my reply was the same as on the former occasion.

"I don't think I can. I know I can."

Looking back on those days, I am afraid I must have been a pretty cocksure young man. But it must have been apparent to Mr. Tillinghast and to Mr. Griswold that there was more behind my statements than mere cocksureness. At any rate the latter immediately put me to work on my own ideas and also assigned George Griswold to work with me. This was a great break for both of us, as we had become fast friends and we went at our new task with so much enthusiasm that in less than a year we had perfected a machine and applied for patents on a device that was destined to play an important part in cash register history.

In those days there were no great corporations as we know them today. The seed was being sown for our present day corporate giants, with unlimited funds and men with sufficient vision to recognize, yes to hunt for, opportunities to introduce improved methods and machines. In 1889, after an inventor had perfected a machine his greatest task was to persuade a lot of Doubting Thomases that it was worth manufacturing.

George Griswold and I were fortunate in numbering among our friends a young man who in modern parlance would have been described as "a live wire". He was just that. His name was Harry F. Baker and he was a traveling salesman or, as we said in those days, a "drummer", for a firm of drug and medicine manufacturers. His territory was all of New England and he made Waterbury his headquarters city.

Harry became as enthusiastic as we were about the cash register, and by dint of talking about it all the time, and describing it to his customers and others as a machine with boundless opportunities, he succeeded in interesting a number of Waterbury men who took stock in a company to make and market it. This was the first Union Cash Register Company.

We started out in a most modest manner. Lacking money to tool for extensive production, we made all our registers by hand. By the time we had made—and sold—about seventy-five registers, we ran out of capital and credit. To raise more money Mr. Baker returned to his native city of Trenton, N. J., where he was successful in getting enough capital to carry on our business in a more substantial way.

So in 1890 we moved to Trenton. George Griswold came along and entered the sales department, while I kept on as superintendent of the plant. The basic difference between the Union cash register and the others on the market at that time was that our machine was deliberately designed for use in general lines of retail business, whereas the others were made for and sold to saloons. As soon as I had seen my first cash register and learned of this limitation of its field the thought had occurred to me that it would be welcomed by retail merchants in all lines, and that thought had been ever present as I developed the register.

The Union was a success from the start. Even in Waterbury, while we were turning out our first handful of machines, we were becoming known.

The first shop built for the manufacture of the Union Cash Register. This was in Water-bury. The author is at the extreme left. Lying on the grass is Mr. George Griswold

CHAPTER IV

In 1892, when our Trenton factory had been turning out cash registers for two years, we received an honor that not only increased the prestige of our register but also was a source of great personal pride and satisfaction to me. The Franklin Institute which was founded in 1824 in Philadelphia as an institution "for the promotion of the mechanic arts," had started in 1834 the custom of awarding certain medals, premiums and certificates for notable inventions. The practice of the committee having charge of these awards was to entertain applications from inventors, manufacturers and others who had machines or devices; these applications requested that the committee investigate the merit of the inventions.

In 1891 we made an application to have our cash register examined on its merits. After the receipt of such an application, the committee first of all would conduct a preliminary examination to determine whether it should be considered favorably or rejected. After the preliminary examination in our case the Franklin Institute notified us that the decision was favorable, and that in due time we would receive an invitation to demonstrate our machine before a subcommittee of the Institute's Committee of Arts and Sciences.

When the invitation finally arrived we were elaborately prepared to show what we had. We had not only our own machine ready to show, but also a competing machine for which the claim was being made that it was much superior to the Union.

"We'll give them both barrels", I said to George Griswold. "We will show them not only that our machine is good, but we will also prove that it is better than any other machine on the market".

On the appointed date we went to Philadelphia with the two registers and for several hours, with the closest attention of every member of the committee, we demonstrated the two machines to the last ounce of our physical powers. When we left that room we were as exhausted as if we had spent the entire time running up the side of a mountain.

But we felt amply repaid for our efforts when we were formally notified that the committee had recommended the award of the John Scott Legacy Medal. This was inscribed "To the Most Deserving" and was officially presented by the City of Philadelphia on the recommendation of the Franklin Institute.

This Franklin Institute having been named in honor of Benjamin Franklin, because of his keen interest and successful experiments in arts and sciences, I was doubly gratified at receiving its medal, for the reason that Benjamin Franklin's father was also my great-great-great-great-grandfather. His name was Josiah Franklin, and he was born December 23, 1657. His first wife was Ann Child whom he married in England and brought to New England in 1684. Of the seven children born to this union, Anne Franklin was one, and Benjamin was one of the ten children of Josiah and his second wife, Abiah Folger. Anne Franklin, who was born January 5, 1686, married John Harris of Ipswich, Mass., and her daughter, Ann Harris, married Jacob Fuller, my great-great-grandfather, in Ipswich, Mass. So when the Franklin medal came to me I was glad to think that I was doing my part to keep it in the family.

It can readily be seen that in the John Scott Medal of the Franklin Institute, the Union Cash Register had an asset of great advertising value. It put a public seal of merit on our cash register and made our job of introducing the machine much simpler than it would otherwise have been. With demand increasing, we applied ourselves to the dual task of marketing the register as it then was and perfecting improvements which were destined to

My first office in Trenton. I left my moustache in Waterbury

bring about a great increase in its usefulness to merchants.

The first cash registers from our Trenton factory had a great many parts which had to be made by hand. They were just what the name implied—cash registers. That is, they made a temporary record of money paid out or taken in, but this was only until another transaction changed the figures. They had no mechanism by which a permanent record could be printed on a tape. The possibility of not only printing a record for the merchant but also supplying a check receipt for the customer was one of the things which I thought about constantly.

We kept steadily at the job of improving the register. I perfected and patented the printing mechanism, and also the device which would give a printed receipt to the customer. There was general agreement, in the cash register business and among users of cash registers, that the Union was the best cash register on the market. But we were continually at a disadvantage because our financial setup was never as good as the register we made. Insufficient capital hampered us. We had several reorganizations, and the company remained solvent, but there never was enough money to do things in a big way. By 1907 we had thousands of cash registers in service, and by this time we had attracted the attention of the great National Cash Register Company in Dayton, Ohio.

It was inevitable that this should happen, and that the National should decide to buy the Union. Our cash register was too good to be allowed to compete, and it had a number of features that the National felt it should have in its own machines. So, after a period of negotiation that brought about a satisfactory offer, the National acquired the Union company and incorporated many of the features of the Union Cash Register in its own product.

Two years later, in 1909, I was invited to join the National Cash Register Company in the invention department. The Union in its final perfection had been the child of my thought, research and experiment, and the opinion at Dayton was that I could apply my ideas to the improvement of the National.

I was as eager to go to Dayton as they were to have me. I knew that in National Cash no problem of expense was ever allowed to intrude itself as an obstacle to progress. I anticipated with great hopes the possibility of working where I was not hampered by lack of money. So I joined the NCR organization.

For the last three years of my eight year connection with National, I was chief inventor. The invention and development work all centered in a department known as Inventions Department Four. During the first five years I was under a man who even then was recognized as one of the brightest geniuses in the field of mechanics, research and invention. When he left National and I was selected to succeed him as head of Inventions Department Four, I was flattered and conscious that I had been asked to fill a pretty big pair of shoes. His name was Charles F. Kettering.

CHAPTER V

When I became a member of the National Cash Register organization, I entered a different world—at least so far as outward circumstances were concerned. As I had anticipated, financial worries were at an end. The company not only had plenty of money, but was willing to spend whatever might be necessary to carry out any desired development.

But inwardly I was living in the same world I had inhabited since my first invention. Problems were constantly presenting themselves for solution and new devices and improvements were constantly springing from my inner consciousness and demanding attention.

In my experience in Dayton I not only improved the existing line of National registers but also brought out what is known as the No. 2000 line, comprised of machines having applications for practically every line of business. This line is still being sold all over the world and includes the leading machines in the cash register business.

One of the most interesting features of my new environment, and one that has remained interesting to the present time, was the widened range of my personal contacts. The National Cash world was a large one, and my connection there not only brought me into touch with many able men who became my friends, but it also put me into a circle which included leaders in many other lines of industry devoted to the discovery, manufacture, and merchandising of the myriad devices to expedite the operations of business which have been perfected since the turn of the century.

As I review those early days a veritable parade of personalities passes across the screen of memory; in effect it is a news reel of the office and store equipment industry of the last third of a century.

It was in Dayton that I became intimately acquainted with John H. Patterson, founder and president of National Cash. The best word I can find to describe him is "unique", which my dictionary defines as "without another of like kind." He certainly was that. He presented a blend of driving energy and active imagination that made him one of the business leaders of his day.

I could write for hours the history of my various experiences with him, but as his biography has been done completely, by abler chroniclers than I, I will confine myself to the narration of one or two things that remain fixed in my memory. One of them nearly cost me my life, due to Mr. Patterson's fixed belief that he was personally responsible for the physical health of every man in his employ, and that whatever benefited his health was certain to be good for every one else. If he derived benefit from horseback riding the entire executive staff of National Cash was likely to become a riding club. This actually happened once, and he caused a large building to be transformed into a riding hall between sunset one evening and sunrise next morning, at a cost of several thousand dollars. There was a heavy layer of tanbark on the floor and all the other appurtenances of a first class riding establishment, and it was used only a few times.

When Mr. Patterson decided one morning that I was looking a little bit under par he ordered me to go forthwith to the Battle Creek sanitarium for a rest and rebuilding. He was a great believer in Battle Creek, as they had done him a great deal of good, and I found it a fine place in every respect. After I had been there several weeks I returned to Dayton to find that Mr. Patterson had had installed a large number of electric bath cabinets that were devised in Battle Creek. He had ordered all executives to use these cabinets whenever they felt a little tired, and they were very popular.

These cabinets were constructed with a large number of electric lights inside, arranged about a stool on which the bather sat, with his head poked through a rubber apron that was buttoned tightly around his neck. The lights were turned on one series at a time until the proper degree of heat had been generated.

One day when I went up for a bath all the cabinets were in use. As soon as one was vacated I went in and sat down. I had no more than buttoned myself in and turned on the first series of lights than I realized that this was going to be too hot a bath. I started to get out when suddenly I felt what I took to be a great gush of steam up through the buttoned up rubber collar. That was the last I remembered until I came to and found myself lying on a rubbing table with every one running about in a panicky way. When the doctor finally came, in response to some one's urgent summons, he had me taken home in an ambulance. Later I found that what I had taken for a jet of steam really had been a rush of blood to my brain. The doctor said it would have killed most men, and complimented me on having a rugged constitution.

The experience had left me so weak and nervous, however, that it was decided I must go away for a long rest. Finally, after trying two or three places where I seemed to get worse, I found myself at the beautiful old Hotel Chamberlain at Old Point Comfort, Virginia, which enjoyed a well deserved reputation as one of the world's finest hotels. This famous old resort has been burned down and a new one now stands on its former site. I have not visited the new one, but something tells me that however fine it may be, there is gone forever a fine flavor of tradition with which the old building had been permeated through years of use by an appreciative clientele.

The Chamberlain, when I arrived, was so comfortable and luxurious that it seemed as if I would make a complete recovery in a hurry. But my nerves continued to be jumpy—so much so that I could only stand it to remain in one room for one day and night. Every morning Mrs. Fuller would go personally to the desk and say that I felt I would have to be changed to another room. She became a bit sensitive about this, and one morning explained to the room clerk that all the rooms were perfect, but that I was so nervous that I could not stay in one room more than a few hours.

Then we got a demonstration of real Southern hospitality. Instead of dismissing me from his mind as probably just a crank, the clerk found an immediate solution of my difficulty. Explaining to Mrs. Fuller that because it was the off season the hotel had a lot of unoccupied rooms, he said:

"As a matter of fact, we have an entire floor with no one living on it. The rooms are all made up, ready for immediate use. So you tell Mr. Fuller we will move him up there, and whenever he wants to change his room he can do so. In the middle of the night, if he wants to move, he can just walk to any door he sees. It will be unlocked and there he will find another room all ready for him. Tell him it will be all right if he sleeps in five or six rooms every night."

Strangely enough, or perhaps naturally enough, as soon as we were moved to that floor I began to be able to live contentedly in one room, and completed my convalescence in the most delightful surroundings that could be imagined.

Another of my experiences with Mr. Patterson came when my daughter, Lucy May, was married at our home in Dayton. So many guests were expected that we had set up a large tent adjoining the house, in which the wedding supper was to be served. Mr. Patterson had appointed himself master of ceremonies and he took as much interest in every detail of the arrangements as if it had been his own wedding. We had an electrician at work for more than half a day wiring the tent for lights; the caterers were all ready to serve an elaborate wedding supper; everything had gone like clockwork and Mr. Patterson was walking about, rubbing his hands and expressing his satisfaction with all the arrangements, when—with scarcely a moment's warning—a thunderstorm that was almost a cloudburst put out the electric lights. The telephones went out of commission at the same time. We couldn't even get a connection that would enable us to find out how long the lights would be off.

It looked for a few minutes as if the wedding supper would not be served. Mr. Patterson was in a fine frenzy. Having been so intimately connected with all the advance arrangements, he took it as a personal affront that such a mishap should occur. While he was steaming about, making almost as much noise as the storm, the caterer's men began to place wax candles at all the places at the tables. There were more than enough to go around, and when they were all lighted the tent was far prettier than it would have been with the electric lights. Mr. Patterson was delighted:

"Now how did this happen?" he wanted to know. "Some one certainly must have used his head. Mr. Fuller, I want to congratulate you on getting us out of a real difficulty."

I accepted the congratulations. It didn't seem necessary to tell him that I didn't know how it had happened. I was as much in the dark as he was about how the candles happened to be ready, and it was not until later that I found out that Lucy May's wedding had been the beneficiary of one of those odd bits of luck that sometimes happen. It seems that after the electrician had finished wiring the tent he had told Mrs. Fuller he would be glad to do any errands that were necessary at the last minute. The women had just decided that it would be nice to have a few candles at the bride's table, so Mrs. Fuller had asked him to stop at the grocery and ask the grocer to send up some candles. When he got to the store the grocer's boy was out, and the electrician didn't know exactly how many of the candles Mrs. Fuller wanted.

"Tell you what," said the grocer. "Just take take all the

candles there are and tell Mrs. Fuller she can send back all she doesn't need."

So when the electrician had come back he was loaded down with candles. He had boxes of them. The women were sorry he had so many, but rather than ask him to carry them back they had had him put them in a closet, and when the lights went out some one remembered the candles and the supper was saved.

Later the minister said to me: "Now, Mr. Fuller, I see another evidence of the hand of the Lord in the fact that you had all those candles ready when the lights went out."

"Well, Doctor", I replied, "I cannot agree with you. If the Lord had really been interested in our wedding I don't think He would have sent the storm just then."

CHAPTER VI

Soon after my arrival in Dayton I began to be conscious of an unusual personality that stood out even amidst the galaxy of stars which had been attracted by the modern methods and progressiveness of the National Cash Register Company. Recognized throughout the organization as a dynamic leader, Thomas J. Watson as sales manager was inspiring the men in the field with a substantial measure of his own energy, confidence and tirelessness. His methods were meeting with such signal success, as manifested in the constant upward swing of the curve of sales, that he frequently was the topic of conversations in departments only remotely connected with sales. The inventions department was especially conscious of him because of his habit of sending along suggestions for machine design and performance that he thought would make the National line more acceptable to the buying public.

As my acquaintance with Mr. Watson ripened I began to understand why it was that I had been moved to admiration of his unusual personality through watching him preside over the conventions of the Hundred Point Club, composed of salesmen from all over the world who would be brought into the factory each year as a reward for excellent records. Whenever I had had any personal contacts with Mr. Watson I had found him pleasant and agreeable and greatly interested in every phase of the business. As our acquaintance progressed to friendship I discovered that he was a man of wider interests, and of wider *interest* in everything worth while, than any one I had ever met.

My succession to Dr. Kettering's post threw me into still closer contacts with Mr. Watson. He had been, and still is, a close friend of Dr. Kettering, and often had come into Department

Four to discuss matters of invention and improvement. He continued this practice and I grew to have great respect for his vision. He knew what he wanted machines to do, and he could explain his wishes so clearly that I, as inventor, could strive intelligently to give him what he wanted. And when I was successful he was most appreciative. It was on this sort of business relationship that we built up the closer personal friendship which brought him to our home as a frequent guest. He and Mrs. Fuller found much in common. Both had a wide range of interests outside their everyday activities and they were alike in a desire to help others, especially young people, to better themselves.

When Mr. Watson decided to leave the National Cash to take over the management of the Computing-Tabulating-Recording Company, now the International Business Machines Corporation, we were all much cast down at the thought that this would take him away from Dayton. But we sensed that his talents demanded a wider field, and we saw him depart for New York with confidence that he would find new heights and would scale them successfully.

CHAPTER VII

From the beginning in 1909, my connection with the National Cash Register Company had given me a wide range in inventive activity.

My original assignment at Dayton was to finish the model of a cash register on which I had been working for the Union in Trenton, before it was purchased by National Cash. This model I completed and Patent No. 1,117,179 was the result. I also worked on a number of other schemes before becoming chief inventor, and these became patents Nos. 1,022,230 and 1,122,489.

When I took charge of Invention Department No. 4, my principal task was the development of the No. 1200 line. This was the line that later was known as the No. 2000. Three or four years work on this line of machines resulted in models which I built for twelve or thirteen different businesses. They are still the leaders of the National line and are the greatest sellers of all cash registers.

When the work on these models was completed, I redesigned the entire No. 2000 line, overcoming some of the difficulties of manufacture and faults of construction. This redesigning bore fruit in patents Nos. 1,725,829, 1,756,350, 1,761,718 and others. So far as I know the machines covered by these patents have never been marketed.

The year 1917, in the spring of which the United States entered the World War, marked the termination of my connection with the National Cash Register Company. My resignation, in September, was dictated by my desire to accept a position which seemed to offer even greater opportunities than I had had in Dayton.

This position was offered me by the Remington Arms Company, which had invested $16,000,000 in a rifle factory in Bridge-port, Conn. Realizing that the war would be over in a year or two, this company was looking around for a peace time business that would keep its factory going and its men employed after the necessity for munitions manufacture had passed. They had decided upon cash registers, largely because there were about a dozen former National Cash Register men holding important executive posts in the arms factory.

I went at my new task with enthusiasm. I had long wished to return to the East, where my relatives and many old friends lived. Bridgeport was near my birthplace in Norwich, and my daughter and her husband were living in Trenton. Besides, one of the conditions of my bonus was that my new register should be ready in ten months, and that was a challenge to my ability that I accepted with pleasure because for a long time I had been nurturing some radically new ideas about the design and construction of cash registers and this gave me an opportunity to put them into effect.

So, as chief inventor in the Remington's cash register line, I developed inside the stipulated time limit a register known as the Remington, which was a success from the moment it was placed on the market.

The machine was designed especially to meet what we had rightly foreseen as a new demand—a register that could be operated by a maimed person. The press down key registers then on the market required that all the keys should be operated together, thus employing the fingers of both hands in a rather complicated operation before a transaction could be registered. The new Remington was a press down key machine that was easily operable with one hand.

We believed that after the war a large number of returned soldiers who had been maimed would come into retail establishments in jobs that would require them to use cash registers of the press down key type, which would be impossible for them unless such a register as the new Remington was available. This proved to be the case.

The total time required to put this machine on the market was about four years. After the first fifty had been made, largely by hand, the seat of manufacture was moved to Ilion, N. Y., where the Remington company had a large arms factory that it decided to transform into a cash register plant.

Soon after the success of this register was assured, I made up my mind to retire from active work. This was in 1925, just fifty years after I had taken my first job in the paper mill in Norwich. I made up my mind that a half century of steady work had entitled me to spend the rest of my days in leisure.

But complete retirement, after one has been as active as I had been all my life, is not the ideal state that is so fondly imagined. Time drags. The lack of definite objectives seems to turn life sour. Too much leisure eventually becomes a most boring condition.

Just about the time I was beginning to realize this, I happened to meet Mr. Watson, whom I had not seen for several years. In the course of our conversation he asked what I was working on at the moment, and when he learned that I had retired he was most emphatic in stating that this was all wrong. Complete retirement, he said, was the road to quick and complete disintegration. He invited me to join the inventions staff of the International Business Machines Corporation. This was in 1927, and every day that has passed since then has shown me what a mistake I would have made if I had persisted in remaining in retirement. For I accepted his invitation with alacrity and thus opened up for myself the widest field of invention, with the greatest possible support and cooperation, that it has been my good fortune to encounter.

Perhaps this is the best place I will find, in writing this little story of my life, to digress from the subject of Fred Fuller and write a few words on the subject of Thomas J. Watson, whose friendship I value as one of the richest and most satisfying experiences of my life. Already I have narrated some of the circumstances of our earlier days, and told how confident we were when he left Dayton, nearly twenty-five years ago, that he would go onward to a brilliant future.

Now that he has lived up to and exceeded all our predictions, I am proud and glad that the old association has been renewed and that the last works of my life will be in cooperation with his one real ambition—to increase the extent to which machines can be made to lift the burdens of drudgery from the shoulders of men, so that all may live a fuller, freer and richer life.

The keynote of Mr. Watson's life is service. No one who knows him even slightly can doubt that. I don't think there is a man alive who is more eager to better the common lot of mankind, regardless of race, creed, or color. I am sure that he is among the world's leaders in actual accomplishments toward that end.

The world knows him best as a man who has succeeded, but he is wholly unwilling to accept that definition of himself. How often I have heard him say: "The minute we say to ourselves that we have succeeded, we have confessed failure. If we say that we are succeeding, that may be true and is a healthy condition—but when a man is satisfied that he has succeeded, he means that his striving for success is over, and that marks him as a failure. This life is worth while only as it holds a promise of doing things better—a man who is doing his best each day is truly alive, but a man who did his best yesterday is starting to die."

The Watson trait that I find most engaging, the trait I think shows the real man most clearly, is his belief in friendship as one of life's great gifts. I well remember a speech I heard him make on this subject, before a group of more than a thousand members of the International Business Machines organization. There were no guests present from outside the company. It was in a very real sense a family talk.

"We should always remember," said Mr. Watson, "that our greatest capital is found in true friendships. I have been broke, financially, twice in my life. But I always had many friends, and I did not let my financial troubles worry me unduly. I never ran very fast after money when I saw it getting away from me. But whenever I found a friendship in danger I always acted with all the speed at my command to save it. Friendship is a more valuable asset than anything else in the world. I would like every person in our organization to realize that. It is one of the facts of life that we should hold in our minds at all times.

"When you have built capital in the form of good friends, you should guard it more closely than financial gains. I could not bear the thought that something might happen during the remainder of my life that would reduce my capital of friends. I have made friends in many walks of life and in many countries. But I want to say here tonight, in all sincerity, that the friends I prize most highly are my associates in IBM throughout the world.

"Let us all try to be more friendly. And let us extend our friendships outside of our own organization. As citizens of the world we owe an obligation beyond the limits of our own business. I feel that IBM is doing a real work in bringing about better understanding among the peoples of the seventy-nine countries in which we operate."

Fate was kind to Mr. Watson in endowing him with an exceptionally fine mind. It is true that all men are born equal when it comes to the number of their members—eyes, ears, arms, legs, etc.—but it is the scheme of creation that the mental endowment conferred varies greatly. A fine mind, active and resourceful, in a healthy body, was the most important capital that the present head of IBM possessed when he started. He has increased the quality and capacity of his mind, and preserved the health of his body by exercising them both with real profit.

One of my first experiences with the dynamic quality of his mentality came back in Cash Register days in Dayton, in the winter of 1911. One of the service men appeared in Inventions Department Four with an armful of signs. Each bore just one word—THINK. He started to tack them up in various locations, where they were arrestingly visible to every man in the room, and to every one entering the department.

"What are those for?" I asked him.

"That's a new slogan. The advertising department says Mr. Watson has ordered them put up all over the factory."

THINK. That was what we were being paid for. It was what we did in that department. We thought and thought, and finally our thoughts took shape in sketches that became drawings that became models that became patents. THINK—it was our very life. But I do not think, until those signs went up, that we had thought much about thinking, and I am sure that after they were posted we found them, in some mysteriously intangible way, a real stimulus to closer thinking. When later on I heard the story of how this slogan came to life from the clear brain of Mr. Watson, I realized gradually that it represented a fine bit of applied psychology.

It was the practice of the sales and advertising departments at National Cash to hold a meeting every morning, at which new ideas and suggestions were developed to help the sales and advertising effectiveness. Mr. Watson was at the head of the two departments. One morning there didn't seem to be one idea in the entire assemblage, and there were some of the best brains in the sales and advertising world gathered in that meeting room. It seemed as if the meeting would have to adjourn with nothing to its credit. And then, as it was told me later by a friend of mine who was in the meeting, Mr. Watson leaped to his feet and hastily mounted the platform. There was no stenographer present, and his exact words were not taken down, but from notes made informally it seems that he said about this:

"The trouble with all of us is that we don't THINK enough. We are not paid for working with our feet—we draw salaries for working with our heads. Feet can never compete with brains.

"Thought has been the father of every advance since time began.

"Knowledge is the result of thought, and thought is the keynote of success in this business and in every other business.

"Every man on the selling force of this business today would make two dollars where he now only makes one, if he would but THINK along the right lines.

" 'I didn't think' has cost the world millions of dollars."

It was then that Mr. Watson had ordered the signs printed and put up all over the factory. They were sent to the field offices. The slogan was so simple, and so unusual, that the signs began to attract attention outside the company. Many requests were received for them. And when Mr. Watson moved from Dayton to his larger field of activity he took the slogan with him. Today there is no IBM office, service department or other workshop, without its THINK sign. We have them in our laboratory. Trite as it may sound, after gazing at THINK signs for many years, I can still find inspiration when faced with a knotty problem, by simply sitting back and looking at this magic word a minute or two and then proceeding to put its advice to work, perhaps along an entirely new line of reasoning. Mr. Watson's company now publishes THINK Magazine, which goes out every month to tens of thousands of thoughtful readers.

THINK signs have been supplied to thousands of outside offices. No man knows how much they have contributed to the world's welfare, but surely it is a considerable amount.

CHAPTER VIII

To go back to 1927; when Mr. Watson invited me to join the invention staff of IBM I was both pleased and flattered. This company had been forging ahead so rapidly, both in sales volume and in the number of new and useful machines it had brought out, that its reputation had spread to all parts of the world. Its annual balance sheet showed year after year that it was wisely and profitably managed. I had learned at Dayton that the Watson belief was that anything worth doing was worth doing in the best way. Added to my natural delight at renewing my association with Mr. Watson was an equally natural satisfactoin that I was to become a part of his progressive organization. I lost no time in accepting his invitation.

He insisted, however, that before I started to work I must dictate the terms of a contract that would be entirely satisfactory to me. He wanted me to feel secure in every way, so that I could devote myself to invention with no worries about my standing in the company. He sent me to the IBM legal department to tell what I thought would be fair, and when they had drafted a contract along the lines I suggested he signed it without change of a single word. I embarked on my new duties with an enthusiasm compounded partly of relief that I was no longer in retirement and partly, as may well be imagined, because I had returned to active work in an inventor's paradise.

By this I mean that one of the prime policies of IBM under Mr. Watson's leadership is that inventors are to be given every possible aid and encouragement. He believes, and frequently says, that the world must continue to progress through research and invention. In that belief he will back a new idea to the limit, once he is convinced it has merit. His vision alone is responsible for the presence in the IBM line of many important machines, now indispensable to business, which others had said could not possibly be made.

Just how much of an inventor's paradise IBM really is will be realized when consideration is given to the tremendous number of machines this company manufactures and sells for the assistance of business and industry. There is a wonderfully complete line of electric bookkeeping and accounting machines, which operate on the punched card principle. Another division manufactures electric time systems so marvelously conceived that a master clock not only actuates secondary clocks at any distance away, but also supervises their correctness at hourly intervals. This division also makes time recorders, time stamps, central control radio and speech equipment, intercommunicating telephone systems, fire alarm systems, watchman's clocks and similar devices.

Then there is a division to manufacture an all-electric writing machine which not only increases the speed of typewriting but also removes the fatigue factor, and another division which makes a radio typewriter, on which Rear Admiral Byrd sent a message from Little America. Still another division makes industrial scales, which include an accounting scale and a unit-counting scale, each of which is a marvel of efficiency.

The proof machine for banks, which will be described fully later on, is the product of another division.

With more than a thousand individual machines, it will readily be apparent that a mind as active as Mr. Watson's must find a fertile field for speculation on possible extension of their uses, and of new machines for many purposes. It is always a pleasure to me to get a message that Mr. Watson would like to have me drop into his office the next time I am in New York, for I know that such a summons often means that he has thought of a problem which he wants to pass along to me.

We sit at his desk and he outlines his ideas to me. Then I

go away and think them over, and when I feel that I have worked out something practical we go over it again. That is the way many IBM machines have been born, and the way many others will come into being.

My first invention with IBM was the acme of simplicity. One of the divisions of the company at that time was the Dayton Scale Company, which has since been combined with the Hobart Manufacturing Company of Troy, Ohio, the IBM being part owner of the new company. The principal product in the Dayton line was a computing scale, which told the merchant how much to charge the customer, and also enabled the customer to see that the price charged was in harmony with the weight and rate per pound.

Computing scales today are as familiar to most people as telephones or any of the other conveniences of modern life. They were not exactly a mystery to me either, for in the early days of my inventive career, way back in 1895, I had patented one of the first ones. A few years later I brought out another computing scale, which presented one of the most difficult engineering problems I have ever had to solve. Without being too technical, I can describe the difficulty by saying that it forced me to machine a hyperbolic paraboloid surface from a steel bar. This was even harder than it sounds.

It was not until I had established contact with Professor Cook, who taught astronomy in Princeton University, that I knew there was such a thing as a hyperbolic paraboloid. I went to him after numerous failures in an attempt to make a part which would move my price indicator, and he soon discovered that I was trying to make a curve in two planes. In one plane it would be a hyperbole and in the other a parabola. He was of the opinion that this could not be done. However, as we talked it over I got an idea of how to do it, and finally I succeeded. I machined a piece of steel so that it was level on the bottom and

Photo by Arnold Genthe

We sit at Mr. Watson's desk and he outlines his ideas to me. Then I go away and think them over. That is the way many IBM machines have been born.

carried this hyperbolic paraboloid surface on the upper side. Then I found it would be better to roll it up—that is, to machine the hyperbolic paraboloid on the surface of a cylinder that would revolve on my computing mechanism in contact with another metal piece that would cause the dial recordings to be accurate.

This scale, on which I received Patent No. 655,899, was never marketed in the United States, but had a wide sale in England. It was so sensitive and accurate that a butcher using it would set up the weight of the wrapping paper on the tare beam before weighing the meat to be wrapped, so that the final price computation would enable the customer to pay for the meat alone.

Some time after I had worked out my hyperbolic paraboloid and shown it to Professor Cook, an astronomer from Yale University came to see me in Trenton. He said he had heard of my success and thought I might be able to devise a similar mechanism to aid him in astronomic calculations.

"How much would you wish to multiply," I asked him. He said nine digits multiplied by nine digits would be the top.

"Well, Professor," I said, "after the troubles I have had perfecting a device to multiply two digits by two digits, I am obliged to recommend that you retain your sanity by refraining from any attempt to make a similar machine with the capacity you require."

When I joined the IBM the Dayton Scale Division was struggling with the problem of enlarging the figures on its computing scale so that the merchant could read them more easily, and especially so that a short clerk, say five feet tall, would get the same result as a man six feet tall. There had been complaint that the figures could not be read easily, and especial complaint that the different angles of vision for clerks of different height caused different readings of the chart. The actual printed figures on the drum could not be enlarged, without making a drum so big that it would not fit on a scale. The desired result must be attained by resorting to a different system of figure magnification.

The credit for the final solution of this difficulty belongs to Mr. Watson. I was at the main office on some other business when he sent for me to come in and see him. He wanted a small magnifying glass put on the scale, that would cover up all the figures except one row. In this way the operator could select the proper figures more quickly. We had quite a discussion on this point. To arrange a glass as suggested would require a very close and accurate setting, or the small opening would not coincide with the proper column of price figures. Also the operator would have to stand in an exact straight line with the figures behind the glass. I explained this but Mr. Watson thought it would fill the bill and we therefore started to put this sort of device on a regular model of the Dayton scale. Before we had gone very far I was sure we had started on the wrong track, but we finished the scale just as Mr. Watson had asked for it. Before demonstrating the scale I obtained a magnifying glass five inches in diameter and arranged to mount it in the same frame as the smaller glass. With this apparatus it was not necessary to bother with a special aperture. Consequently the glass did not have to be adjusted as accurately and could be set more quickly by the clerk without calling for much thought.

I took the completed model down to Mr. Watson's office for a demonstration, keeping the large glass in my pocket. He congratulated me on having picked that particular day for my visit, saying that a number of the executives in the Dayton Division were in New York for a sales conference. We set up the scale and I explained it first to Mr. Watson. I could see from his expression that it had fallen short of his expectations, but he called the Dayton delegation in and we went through the demonstration again. They also failed to manifest much enthusiasm, and after a few perfunctory remarks started back into their conference. Mr. Watson was conferring with them at the door of his office as I hastily slipped the large magnifying glass onto the scale. I called him out of the group for a moment and showed him the new idea. He immediately grew enthusiastic. He called the Dayton men over and explained it to them, and they also were greatly pleased. I had orders at once to rush the invention, and of course I worked with enthusiasm to complete the model. The improvement was patented and placed on the scale. It took the retail public by storm. The new scale, called the Magniscope, was the deciding factor in enabling a Scale salesman to elect himself president of that year's IBM Hundred Percent Club by having the largest percentage of his quota of any salesman in any division. The Magniscope increased the sale of the line of scales to which it was applied by the impressive total of 75 per cent in its first year on the market.

At that time the entire experimental laboratory of the IBM was housed on Varick Street, in downtown New York. With the advent of the depression Mr. Watson set to work on a project that had long been in his mind—a general laboratory of research and invention at the IBM plant in Endicott, N. Y. He reasoned correctly that with materials down in price, and men in the building trades largely unemployed, he could serve a double purpose by building at this time. He would get his laboratory at the lowest possible cost and give employment to a large number of men who otherwise would be out of jobs.

The splendid laboratory at Endicott was the result, and the Varick Street staff was moved up there. But I personally did not wish to go to Endicott, for the reason that I was working on something of great importance and felt that closer proximity to Mr. Watson would be advantageous. This was the machine now being used by banks throughout the country for sorting and totaling foreign checks—known as the IBM Proof Machine for Banks. So Mr. Watson directed me to fit up a laboratory in Orange, N. J. This was only a few minutes out of New York, and close to my home in Llewellyn Park. I assembled a staff and worked independently on the proof machine. The conception and development of this machine is a story by itself.

Another story, which cannot be told at present, concerns the seven projects of major importance which are now being developed in our laboratory and will sooner or later become public as new machines or improvements to machines now in use.

CHAPTER IX

At about the time that I joined the IBM another man made his debut in the organization. His name was Frank McKennett. He had a background of years of experience in banking, and had come to IBM because, after observing the workings of its electric bookkeeping and accounting machines in the bank where he was employed, he was convinced that greater opportunities lay in this field than in any he had yet seen.

When Mr. McKennett joined the IBM sales force he was presented to Mr. Watson, who never overlooks an opportunity to discuss special fields of industry, finance and education with any representatives of those fields. Mr. Watson asked Mr. McKennett what important job there was in banks that could not be done by existing machines.

During one period of his banking experience Mr. McKennett had worked on the sorting of "foreign" checks—a foreign check does not necessarily have to be from another country, merely from another bank. He had often thought that some machine should be devised to perform this tedious task better than it could be done by hand, which would result in the release of bank clerks from one of the most onerous tasks in their daily routine. So Mr. McKennett told Mr. Watson he thought such a machine could be invented, although he himself had no idea how it could be designed.

After getting Mr. McKennett's idea firmly in mind Mr. Watson talked it over with me. I went down to the seclusion of Atlantic City for a period of preliminary thought, as a result of which I produced a set of sketches that I handed over to the draughting room. They were widely removed from what finally emerged from my thinking, but at any rate they were a start.

To explain the underlying idea of this machine it may be well to discuss briefly the long established routine by which banks had been accustomed to handling "foreign" checks. This term is applied to checks cashed in any bank and drawn on another bank. The word foreign in this usage does not mean from another country. If two banks are located next door to each other, the checks of either are just as "foreign", when cashed by the other, as if the banks were thousands of miles apart.

The receiving teller of a bank, whose duty it is to accept deposits of both cash and checks, receives each day a considerable number of the latter. These must all be listed and all must be examined and sorted according to classification designations. The old system makes it necessary for each teller to sort the checks by hand, separating them into a series of boxes or other receptacles. At the end of each sorting operation each box, if no error has been made, contains checks or drafts of the same classification. After the checks have been correctly sorted they are passed to the printing mechanism of an endorsing machine, which puts on the name of the bank.

The sorting operation is laborious and difficult. Considerable manual effort is required and because of the large number of sorting boxes many of them are distantly located from the operator, beyond the normal reach of his hand. The inconvenience of this arrangement naturally results in frequent errors, the correction of which slows up the sorting operation.

Mr. McKennett worked very closely with me. In order that I might be familiar with the condition I was seeking to improve, he took me to a few banks where we watched the operation of sorting and classifying foreign checks. Every one we talked with agreed that it was one of the most laborious operations in banking, and of course it was of first importance that there should be no errors either in classifying the checks or totaling the amounts they represented.

The proposition was especially fascinating because there was no machine in existence which could be used. It was virgin territory. I sat at my desk for hours thinking out ways and means. Every time I looked up I would see a sign that bore the magic word THINK. As I walked about the laboratory, or went down to the main office, that THINK sign kept presenting itself to my vision. And THINK I did.

At first I had tried to visualize a mechanism that would take the checks to their proper pockets. One objection after another bobbed up. It could be done, but not in any simple way. The thing was rapidly becoming one of the most difficult problems I had ever encountered.

"By George," I said to myself, "this is almost as hard as that old hyperbolic paraboloid." While I was letting my mind rest I would frequently muse over past experiences in invention, and the instant that this hyperbolic paraboloid came into my thoughts I was on the track of the solution I sought for the bank machine. I didn't recognize it instantly, but when I finally recalled how I had simplified that old scale device by rolling it up on the outer edge of a cylinder I found that on the desk tablet in front of me I had absent mindedly sketched a wheel. Something about the wheel arrested my attention and I began to put a series of pockets around the inside of the circumference. Check pockets! I would stop trying to take the checks to the pockets. Instead I would use a wheel to bring the pockets to the checks.

After a few more rough sketches I called in an artist and had him make a finished drawing of the machine itself. Not any of the necessary mechanism, of course. Just a picture of a machine, as if it had all been completed. This was the way I imagined it would look when it was completed. All I had to do now was put in the works.

It has been my continuing experience that the most difficult part of a new invention is the discovery of the proper starting point. All the basic fundamentals of mechanics were discovered and handed down to us by the ancients. When Archimedes discovered the principle of the lever, and when some anonymous, primitive scientist learned how to apply the principle of the wheel, the ground work was laid for the utilization of water power, then of steam and finally of electricity, radio activity and all the other natural forces that man has bent to his wishes and his needs down through the centuries.

Having found the correct starting point for the proof machine in July, 1928, I worked along, step by step, until on October 21, 1930, the final papers for the first patent application were prepared, consisting of ten closely printed sheets of text and ten detail drawings. This was to be followed by other applications for broader patent protection. The point I am trying to emphasize is that it required only a little more than two years to start from nothing but an idea and arrive at a complete machine in which were embodied many new applications of ancient mechanical principles.

Another point I would like to emphasize in this connection is that I had passed my sixty-seventh birthday when I started work on this invention, and that by the time the first machine was installed for actual use in a bank I was more than seventy years old. But of course I am old fashioned. I understand from reading the newspapers that when a man reaches forty years of age he is considered too old to get a job, and will not be reemployed if he is unfortunate enough to lose the position he has held up to that age. It was fortunate for me that this great truth had not been permitted to leak out before my fortieth birthday. It might have prevented nearly four score patented and profitable inventions that stand to my credit since that date, to say nothing of some current inventions on which patent applications are either pending or in preparation, which will bring my score up to more than 100 patents—80 per cent of them issued after my fortieth birthday!

The preliminary studies of banking practice in which I engaged prior to starting on the proof machine opened my eyes as nothing else could have done to the tremendous volume of business done in the United States by check. Of course I knew, as every one does, that when the New York Clearing House handles hundreds of millions, in fact, many billions of dollars in its annual transactions, the check volume must be large, but it was not until I was taken through some of the large New York banks that I learned how large it was.

The checks received by the paying and receiving tellers are all sent to what is called the Rack Department. Here they are first sorted by weight! Each block, to be handled by the sorting clerks, weighs five pounds. The manual system starts with the sorting of those checks into the proper boxes, one for each bank that is a member of the Clearing House Association, which includes most of the banks in the metropolitan area, and others for out-of-town banks. After the checks have been sorted by hand they are listed on adding machine tapes and a total is obtained for each bank. Then the checks are sent to the Clearing House, the bank retaining one set of records and sending another to the Clearing House, where all the representatives of member banks meet, each with his own supply of foreign checks. These are exchanged among the representatives and the totals are entered in the settling clerk's statement. The checks are taken back to the banks on which they were drawn. This of course is a very sketchy description of the operation, but it will serve the situation to which I addressed myself. How to end a large part of this drudgery and enable the sorting clerks to be used to better advantage in something more productive.

The proof machine as I finally evolved it, and as it is now used by banks, consists first of all of a wheel having twenty-four pockets. Each of these pockets represents a bank. Each bank has its own adding machine. Then there are three other adding machines, one to give the total of any compartment; one of any desired group of compartments, and one for a grand total.

When a rack clerk is transferred to one of these proof machines he finds himself in a different world. He glances at a check, presses the key of the bank on which it was drawn, and thereby brings the wheel around until that bank's pocket is under a slot large enough to permit the check to be dropped through. Before dropping the check the clerk adds the amount of the check on a ten key adding machine. The bank of keys for the twenty-four banks, and the adding bank, are only a few inches apart. The long reach to the remote pockets is eliminated. The adding is performed as the check is sorted. Compartment totals, group totals and grand totals are available instantly. Moreover, he can handle from 1,400 to 1,800 checks an hour, with no mental or physical strain, compared with the 900 to 1,100 an hour which was his top speed under the manual method.

I was much pleased when the IBM company newspaper, BUSINESS MACHINES, carried the reprint of an article written for "The Great Lakes Banker", official publication of the Illinois Bankers Association. The author of this article was Gaylord S. Morse, President of the Terminal National Bank of Chicago, and he wrote after his bank had had two years of experience with the proof machine. Mr. Morse's article is such a complete description of the uses and advantages of this machine from a banker's standpoint, that I take great pride in reproducing it here. Mr. Morse wrote:

"Marking the first forward step in proof work in many years, the International Business Machines Corporation's new proof machine for banks combines the most desirable characteristics of modern deposit proof practice.

"Fundamentally, it embodies the thought expressed by a

Feb. 13, 1931

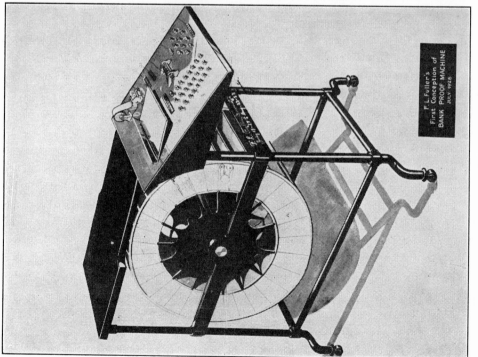

F. L. Fuller's
First Conception of
BANK PROOF MACHINE
JULY 1926

It took three years for the Proof Machine to progress from the original conception, pictured above at left, to the first working model shown at right. When the tremendous number of parts involved and the complexity of operation are considered, this really is an unusually short time.

banker, several years ago, who said in an address before the American Bankers Association: 'It is my hope that some day we shall have a machine that will enable us to list items received for deposit through the clearings and from correspondent banks just as they are listed on the deposits, proving each one, and at the same time sort and produce control figures for each separate division. This may seem fantastic, yet because of the rapid strides in the last few years we cannot help but believe it is at least possible, if not probable.'

"The answer to this banker's hope for a modern mechanical method of proving deposits may be found in the proof machine.

"Deposits are forwarded directly from the machine from the receiving teller or mail teller. No preliminary handling is necessary, because the proof machine sorts, lists and proves deposits in a single simultaneous operation.

"Through the medium of a bank of twenty-four selected keys the proof machine operator controls a rotating drum around whose circumference are located twenty-four compartments or sorting receptacles; similarly these twenty-four keys control twenty-four adding counters which provide twenty-four listings and totals. In addition, a control counter furnishes a continuous listing of the items exactly as they appear on the deposit slip, with a total to compare with each credit total, and an accumulating grand total of all deposits proved.

"Its operation is simplicity itself. The operator depresses the selection key corresponding to the bank on which the check is drawn, lists the amount of the check on the 'touch system' ten-key adding machine, inserts the check in the chute, and depresses the release bar with the following results:

"1. The check is automatically sorted into the proper receptacle or compartment.

"2. The amount of the check is listed on the proper compartment tape, in duplicate if necessary.

"3. The amount is likewise listed on the control tape, together with a symbol identifying the compartment to which the check has been sorted.

"This procedure is repeated with every check in a deposit. When the last check has been listed the operator depresses a total key, and a total is printed on the control tape.

"This total is then compared with the deposit slip, or credit total; any difference that may have occurred, due to errors by depositors or clerk, are localized, since the checks are always listed on the control tape in the same sequence as they are received from the depositor, and the symbol printed opposite the amount of the check identifies the compartment where the check has been sorted and listed.

"With this machine there is no limit to the size of deposits which may be proved, or to the number of checks which may be included in a single block or batch. An operator can prove either a large or small deposit with equal facility, because every item is under control at all times.

"In order to facilitate continuous operation of the machine it is equipped with two warning light signals; a red light which notifies the operator when the supply of paper is running low, and a green light which signals the operator when a sorting receptacle has been filled to capacity.

"The utility of this machine does not end with the proof of deposits. In clearing, items may be sorted and listed to twenty-four bookkeeping sections or ledgers. In fact, any rehandling operation which does not require an excessive number of distributions may be assigned to the machine.

"A supplementary advantage also accrues from the fact that compartment tapes may be used in conjunction with photographs of the items to eliminate the writing of transit letters.

"All these operations are performed at a speed which renders the adaptability of this machine to the average bank's requirements particularly desirable. After a few months experience the ordinary clerk can sort and list 1,400-1,800 items per hour; and where volume permits clerks are handling 6,000-9,000 items per day with the aid of this machine.

"Accurate control over the operators' production can be maintained by means of two item counting devices, one of which is under lock and key.

"It is apparent that the trend of deposit proof operations to-day is toward a simultaneous sorting, listing and proving system. Such a system gives a bank a speedier and more comprehensive command and control of all the phases of check handling, and reduces the cost of the proving and distributing operators by synchronizing, mechanically, the sorting, listing, and proving of deposits.

"The Terminal National Bank of Chicago was one of the first banks in the central west to adopt this new method of proving and assorting items. Our experience with the proof machine covering a period of two years has surpassed all expectations. We also find this method most helpful in our endeavor to minimize the hours of transit department employes."

One of the most valuable features of the proof machine is that it diminishes the proportion of clerical errors in check sorting and listing, and provides the quickest and easiest method ever known for discovering and correcting the occasional errors that do occur. These errors usually occur in the form of figure transposition, due to a momentarily lapse of coordination between eye and hand. In the old, or manual system, when such an error was made the process of locating the mistake was so involved that the general practice was to re-list all the checks, instead of attempting to locate the one incorrectly listed. With the proof machine one has only to put the control tape alongside the tape that came with the checks being handled, and by comparing the amounts the error is readily discovered and the check on which the error was

Here is the Proof Machine, not only complete and working in many banks in all parts of the United States, but as I had the pleasure of watching it at the New York National Business Show

made is easily located for correction, by looking on the left hand margin of the control tape, where a designating symbol is printed to indicate the compartment in which each check is to be found. As the checks have all been sorted into twenty-four different compartments it will be a simple matter to discover the check, in any compartment, on which an error has been made. The correction of the error on the control tape, in red ink, makes the entire sort correct with a minimum of effort.

CHAPTER X

The proof machine had been successfully introduced and was meeting with immediate acceptance when, in November, 1934, I met with an accident which for several months kept me not only bed-ridden, but absolutely motionless. I was trussed up on a fracture bed so firmly that I reminded myself of Gulliver after he had awakened to find himself bound by the Lilliputians. All because of a simple misstep from a stepladder in the laboratory, which happened as I was inspecting a model of one of my later inventions. After falling heavily to the floor, I was in considerable pain, but supposed I had suffered merely a severe shaking up, the effects of which would soon pass away. In that belief I remained in my office, but after two hours during which the pain failed to subside, I was driven home and called a doctor. Suspecting that I had broken my hip, he had X-ray photographs made immediately, and at 9 o'clock that night, ten hours after my fall, these confirmed his opinion.

Immediately there was feverish activity in the Fuller home. It is one of the sad facts of medical practice, and one about which there is little that can be done, that a broken hip is usually fatal to a person who has passed seventy. I learned later that it was with a feeling of utter hopelessness that Mrs. Fuller called the bone setter recommended by our doctor, and also ordered a fracture bed sent up from one of the hospitals, accompanied by a nurse.

Fortunately for my own peace of mind, every one was able to conceal from me the general belief that I would never leave the bed. By the time Mr. Watson got over to see me I was in my fracture bed, and to tell the truth I was not especially uncomfortable. He expressed great satisfaction at the completeness of the arrangements for my care, and ordered everything possible done to insure my recovery. It was four months before they unstrapped me from the bed, and five months before I was able to leave the house, and Mr. Watson, who visited me at intervals, finally said he was much pleased that I had been kept still so long.

"This will add ten years to your life," he said. "You have had a chance to rebuild every tired bone and muscle in your body, and you will see later on that it has been a mighty fine thing for you."

The doctors, who were genuinely surprised at my comparatively speedy recovery, agreed with Mr. Watson, and now, three years after the accident, I can see that he was probably right, as I have never enjoyed much better health than at present.

While I was flat on my back the convention of the IBM Hundred Percent Club was held at the Waldorf Astoria in New York, and Mr. Watson had a special wire run to my bedside from the convention hall, so that I heard many of the speeches and other events on the program over my own loud speaker. This was a delightful experience, as many of the men who were taking a prominent part in the proceedings were well known to me and it was like having them right in my room.

When I was well along toward complete recovery the doctors began to discuss my case with me. They said it was a remarkable one and would be written up in all the medical journals. I replied that it would be all right with me, if they just kept it out of the undertakers' magazines.

Shortly after I had been well strapped up, one of the draftsmen from the laboratory, at Mrs. Fuller's suggestion, made a caricature which showed very clearly my own ideas of an "automatic fracture bed" and how it should be operated. This was ready in time for use as a Christmas card and was sent to all the doctors, nurses and many of my friends, both as a greeting and as an assurance that while I was down, I was not out.

While I was strapped down, with endless hours in which to

Our East Orange Laboratory occupies the second floor of this building. My own commodious and convenient office is shown at right.

do nothing but THINK, I had several good ideas which have resulted in models and patent applications on devices which sooner or later will appear in the IBM line of machines to bring speed, accuracy and economy to modern business. So all of this "idle" time was not wasted, and I think I actually derived some good out of my accident. But as I have since told Mr. Watson, I do not want my life prolonged by any more decades through breaking more of my bones.

Soon after I returned to active duty it became apparent that the laboratory in Orange was too small for all the engineers, draftsmen, and model makers working on the projects under my direction, and Mr. Watson ordered us to find better and more spacious quarters. After a long search we finally discovered an ideal site in a two-story building in East Orange. We now occupy most of the second floor, with excellent light and every facility for the production of models. Here we are all at work on a number of inventions which I have made since perfecting the proof machine. In my own opinion, two or three of these are of greater value and importance than anything I have yet accomplished, but of course they are still in the confidential stage.

In bringing this brief story of my life to a close, I can truthfully say that of all the lessons I have learned from life, the one I believe to be most valuable can be summed up in the words of Mr. Watson which I have quoted a few chapters back, and which I will repeat in the belief that they are worthy to stand beside any other recipe for success and happiness that has come from any source:

"This life is worth while only as it holds a promise of doing things better—a man who is doing his best each day is truly alive, but a man who did his best yesterday is starting to die."

The workroom at the East Orange Laboratory. Above the draughting force; below, the bench workers.

Patents Granted

to

FREDERICK L. FULLER

F. L. FULLER.

DEVICE FOR REGISTERING AND RECORDING THE TIME WORKED BY EMPLOYES AND AUTOMATICALLY COMPUTING THEIR WAGES.

No. 379,865.   Patented Mar. 20, 1888.

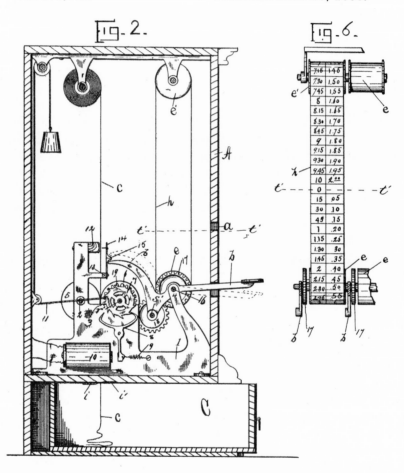

Witnesses.

F. L. Allen.

Tyler J. Howard.

Inventor.

Frederick L. Fuller.

By his Attorney

Frank H. Allen

*I*N REQUESTING a patent on "a certain new and useful improvement in devices for mechanically registering the time worked by employes and automatically computing their wages," Mr. Fuller wrote:

My object is to provide a mechanical device a portion of whose works shall be in constant connection with a motive power, (preferably a clock at the office or other central station,) and which shall also have certain portions of said works adapted to be thrown into engagement with the continuously-moving parts during the time worked by the employe, and to be moved out of such engagement when he ceases work.

F. L. FULLER & G. H. GRISWOLD.
CASH REGISTER AND INDICATOR.

No. 420,554.   Patented Feb. 4, 1890.

Fig. 1.

Witnesses
Wm. F. Tanner
H. D. Shelton Jr

Inventors
Frederick L. Fuller
George H. Griswold
by their attorney
S. H. Hubbard.

*T*HIS was among the first cash registers which displayed to the customer's view the amount he was being charged for a purchase. Today all cash registers have such mechanisms, but in 1890 this was a revolutionary improvement. In the application Mr. Fuller and George H. Griswold his associate, stated:

The objects of our invention are, first, to provide a machine which shall temporarily indicate the amount of each sale, so that the customer may see the same as it appears upon the face of the machine, and which shall, in addition to the temporary indication thus made, transfer the amount of said sale by a process of addition to a premanent totalizing-register, which may be inaccessible to the salesman, and which will at all times show the sum-total of sales to any person having access to the interior of the case without any calculation upon the part of the observer.

F. L. FULLER & G. H. GRISWOLD.
CASH INDICATOR.

No. 420,555.

Patented Feb. 4, 1890.

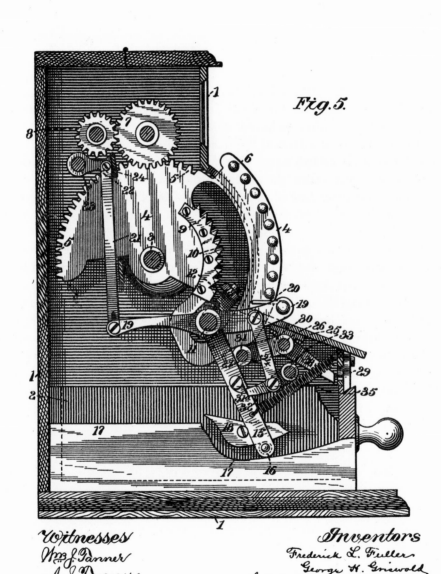

Fig.5.

SEVERAL months after filing their original application for a cash register, Mr. Fuller and Mr. Griswold discovered a method of indicating cash amounts which they believed would result in a better machine. Accordingly they filed a second application in which they said:

Our invention relates to certain new and useful improvements in cash-indicators; but more particularly to machines substantially such as are shown and described in a certain pending application for Letters Patent, Serial No. 305,961, filed April 4, 1889, by the applicants herein named.

The object of our present invention is to amplify and improve in various respects upon the construction shown in the application above referred to, but particularly to provide a stop whereby the mechanism for indicating may be automatically locked when the operating handle or segment has been depressed to the proper distance to furnish a duplex system of locking-teeth for the segments, whose construction and purpose will be hereinafter particularly set forth, to arrange for the locking and unlocking of the money-drawer in proper time, with certain other functions on the machine, and, furthermore, effect a certain interdependence and mutuality of action between the locking mechanism for the indicating devices and the money-drawer.

(No Model.)

4 Sheets—Sheet 2.

F. L. FULLER.

METHOD OF MAKING TIME RECORDS OR PAY ROLLS FOR EMPLOYÉS.

No. 431,344.

Patented July 1, 1890.

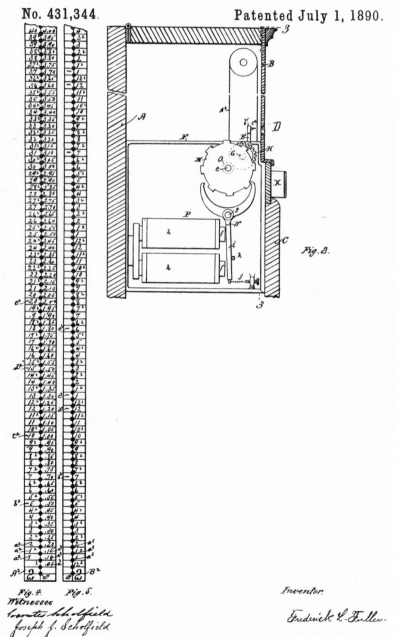

Fig. 2.

Fig. 4. Fig. 5.

Witnesses

Cornelius Scholfield

Joseph J. Scholfield

Inventor.

Frederick L. Fuller.

No. 431,344—*July* 1, 1890.

$\mathcal{A}$LMOST a year and a day after Mr. Fuller had filed his original application for a pay-roll computing time recorder, he completed what he believed was a superior device, having the basic principles of his original machine but involving many improvements in construction and operation. This application, filed while his original request for a time recorder patent was still pending, set forth the object of the invention in the following words:

The object of my invention is to provide a practical method for correctly registering or recording the working-time of employes by means of an instrumentality upon which is notated a series of numbers in arithmetical progression, which will serve to represent the full number of hours of labor performed or amount of wages due; and it consists in moving the said instrumentality forward intermittingly while the employe is at work, and also moving the said instrumentality backward at each consecutive time of working, in order to correct the erroneous register of the said notated instrumentality at the datum-line, due to a necessary excess of forward movement when complying with the practical requirements of factories and workshops.

F. L. FULLER.
WORKMAN'S TIME RECORDER.

No. 435,582.   Patented Sept. 2, 1890.

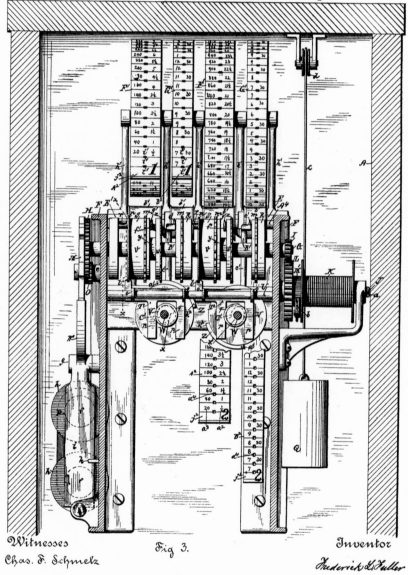

Fig 3.

*T*HIS further improvement in the time recorder was embodied in an application dated only two weeks later than the application for the first improvement, but this patent was not issued until two months after the first application had been awarded. One of the outstanding features of this recorder was the bell or gong, now used on all time recorders, and after noting the greater flexibility of the printed record produced, the inventor described this bell and its purpose in the following paragraph:

It also consists in the additional combination of a bell, going, or other auditory instrument whereby detective notice may be given of the full accomplishment of the engaging or disengaging movement by the employe to other persons in the same room, thus tending to prevent dishonesty in the employe.

(No Model.)

F. L. FULLER.

COMPUTING SCALE OR OTHER CALCULATING MACHINE.

No. 580,783. Patented Apr. 13, 1897

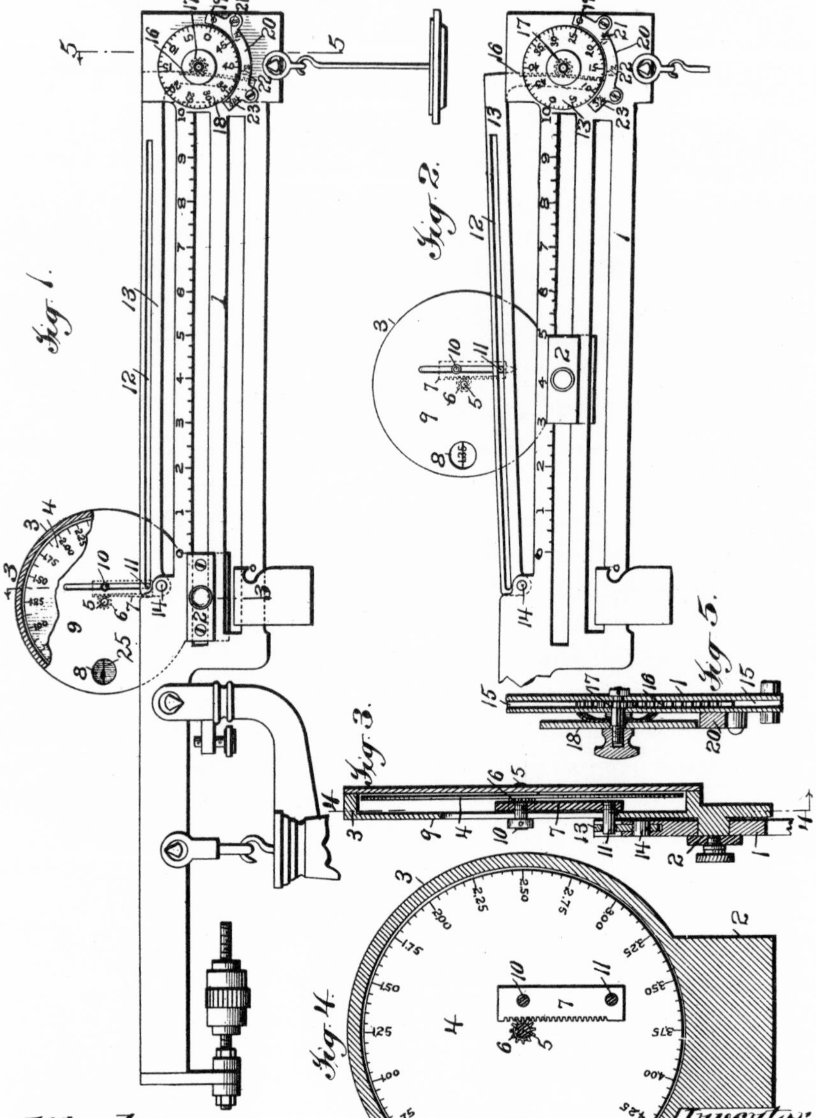
Fig. 1.
Fig. 2.
Fig. 3.
Fig. 4.
Fig. 5.

Attest:
Geo H Botts
G. W. Borst

Inventor
Frederick L. Fuller
By Philipp Munson & Phelps
Attys

*I*N 1895 the range of Mr. Fuller's activities in the field of invention was extended to still another field. Today the computing scale is standard equipment in retail stores of all kinds and sizes, but in the nineties it was a comparative novelity, and far from its present day perfection. Consequently as soon as Mr. Fuller got his first glimpse of a computing scale his interest was aroused and directed toward the possibility of its improvement. So we first find him stating, in his first application for a computing scale patent, that:

This invention relates to improvements in calculating-machines intended for use by accountants or storekeepers, either alone for the purpose of figuring sums generally or to be applied to computing-scales or the like for the purpose of automatically figuring and indicating the cost of goods sold at different rates.

The present invention has for its object the provision of such an apparatus which will have the very important advantage of simplicity and cheapness in construction over practical apparatus of the character heretofore devised and which will also at the same time be absolutely reliable and certain in its operations.

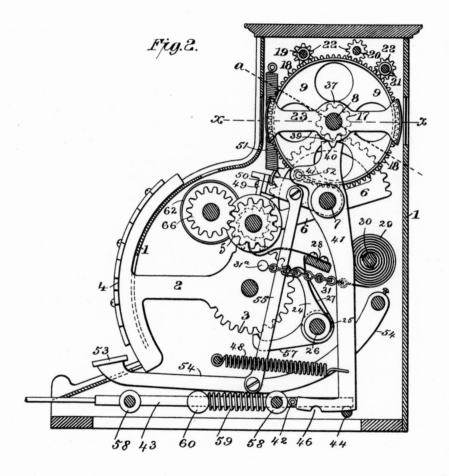

Fig. 2.

*T*HE first cash register patent obtained by Mr. Fuller was notable for the fact that it displayed the amount of the sale so that the customer could read it. But a shortcoming in this device was that the figures were visible only from one side of the machine. Either the customer or the clerk had to go to that side to be sure the correct indication was shown. So in 1891 the Fuller inventive genius was ready to apply for a patent on a device showing the sales figure on *both sides* of the machine. As these figures must read from left to right on each side, it was necessary to have a reversing mechanism, and this was described in the application as follows:

This invention relates to certain novel and useful improvements in cash registers and indicators, but is more particularly designed as an improvement upon the construction shown and described in certain Letters Patent of the United States granted to me jointly with George H. Griswold the 4th day of February, 1890, and numbered 420,554 and 420,555. In the patents just referred to a set of indicating-wheels is provided by means whereof the sum indicated may be shown to the purchaser, but these wheels are visible from one side of the machine only. In my present invention the case is provided with openings both at the front and at the rear, and two sets of indicating-wheels are mounted therein and so connected together that the amount indicated appears both at the front and the rear side of the machine with the figures both right side up and reading properly—that is, from left to right.

Fig.1.

No. 585,468—*June 29, 1897.*

*I*N ORDER to make available to more users the principles behind his first cash register (Patent No. 420,554) Mr. Fuller devoted his next research toward a simple cash register that could be sold at a lower price, while retaining many of the unique and excellent features of the original machine. The result was a machine with a clearly legible customer reading chart, simple in design and operation, which was described in the patent application as follows:

My invention relates to certain new and useful improvements in cash-registers, and has for its object to indicate and register individual sales and to totalize their gross amounts by means of mechanism compact and strong in construction and effective in operation, the required manipulations being of the simplest character and the arrangement of parts being such as to afford ample safeguards against accidental failure to give a correct indication, registration, or totalization, and against wilful or dishonest attempts to fraudulently alter any of such records.

The improvements constituting the present invention are shown herein and will be hereinafter described in connection with a cash-register of the class known as "crank-machines," in which the actuating mechanism consists of a hand-operated shaft provided with clutches for engaging segments which operate indicating-dials, as distinguished from that class of machines commonly termed "key-machines," in which the actuating mechanism consists of a series of keys which, through suitable rack-bars or other similar devices, engage and actuate the indicating devices. It will be understood, however, that many features of the present invention, although shown in connection with such a crank-machine, are equally applicable to key-machines.

F. L. FULLER.
CASH REGISTER.

No. 585,565.   Patented June 29, 1897.

Fig. 1.

Witnesses

Inventor
Fred L. Fuller,
by Penine & Goldsborough
Attorneys

*M*R. FULLER invented another improvement to the cash register which was described in the patent application as follows:

My present invention relates to a modified or improved construction and arrangement of parts embodying the same general or generic mode of operation. More particularly, it involves a general reorganization and rearrangement of the actuating mechanism and the auxiliary devices for locking and releasing the same and introduces important modifications in the clutch mechanism and in the adding mechanism and has especially in view the adaptation of the invention to a register whose indications are read from drums instead of from dials, although it will be readily apparent that many of the features of construction are equally adapted for use in connection with a dial-indicator.

Further features of improvement relate to the mechanism employed for locking and releasing the cash-drawer of the register and for ringing the alarm-bell at the time the drawer is released.

F. L. FULLER.
PRICE SCALE.

No. 602,658.

Patented Apr. 19, 1898.

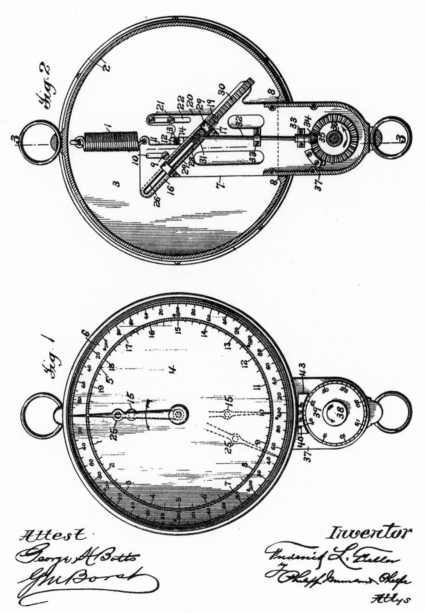

Fig. 2

Fig. 1

Attest.

George A. Betts

G. M. Borst

Inventor

Frederick L. Fuller

by Philipp Emmanuel Okefe

Att'ys

*S*TUDY of the computing scales then on the market (1895-96) led Mr. Fuller to turn his mind to a method of making them more accurate and more dependable over a long period of use. In applying for a patent on a scale improvement he wrote:

This invention relates to that class of scales known as "computing" or "price" scales, in which, in addition to measuring and indicating the weight of an article, the price or cost thereof is also computed and indicated to the purchaser or dealer, or to both.

Scales of this character with computing mechanism actuated by the weighing mechanism, which in turn received its movement from the article weighed, have heretofore been proposed; but in order to secure accuracy in computing these scales have been of such complicated construction as to be liable, owing to the friction and consequent wear of the many parts necessarily employed in their construction, to become easily deranged and inaccurate, particularly after-long-continued use. For these and other reasons, among them the necessarily high cost of the same, due to their complicated construction, scales of this character heretofore devised have been more or less objectionable. It is the object of the present invention to overcome these objections; and to that end the invention consists, briefly, of a computing-scale in which the computing-scale mechanism is actuated by the weighing mechanism through an actuator carried by and moving with the latter, and which actuator is adjustable by means also carried by and moving with the weighing mechanism into position for actuating the computing mechanism in accordance with the unit price of the article weighed.

F. L. FULLER.
INDICATING OR LIKE MECHANISM FOR PRICE SCALES OR OTHER MACHINES.

No. 603,503.   Patented May 3, 1898.

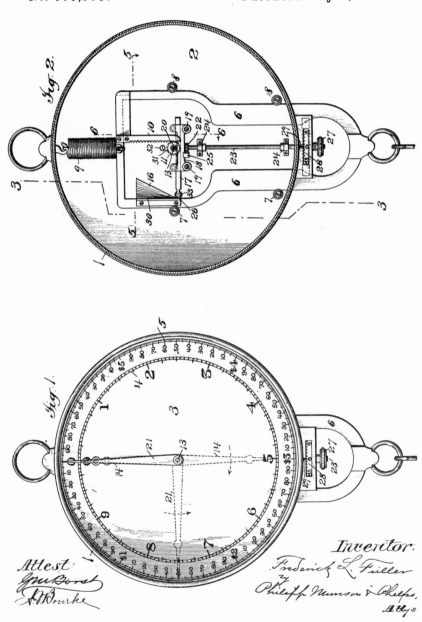

Attest:
GnuBorst
A. U. Bourke

Inventor:
Frederick L. Fuller
by
Philipp Munson & Phelps,
Attys

A YEAR after applying for his second computing scale patent Mr. Fuller was prepared to file another application, in which he stated:

This invention relates to improvements in indicating mechanism designed particularly for application to weighing-scales for the purpose of indicating the prices of articles weighed, it being the object of the present invention to provide mechanism of this character which shall be of simple and durable construction, having few parts, and which shall be reliable and accurate both in adjustment and operation.

Broadly the invention consists in an indicating or like mechanism for application to price-scales and other machines, comprising an inclined member for controlling the extent of its operation and a member coacting therewith, one adjustable transversely to the other, the inclination of the inclined member varying progressively in the direction of such adjustment to suit, in the case of price-scales, variations in the unit price of the articles weighed, so as to secure actuation of the indicating mechanism in accordance with such unit prices. The inclined member of the indicating mechanism is preferably, as will hereinafter appear, the actuator thereof, and the member also which is adjustable in the transverse direction is preferably the member coacting therewith.

F. L. FULLER.
INDICATING OR LIKE MECHANISM FOR PRICE SCALES.

No. 603,504. Patented May 3. 1898.

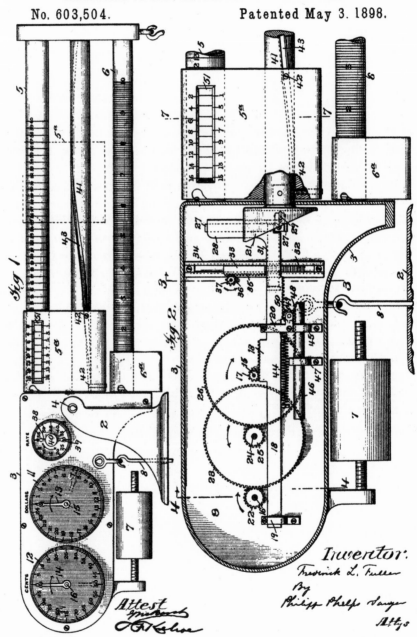

Fig 1.

Fig 2.

Attest

Inventor:
Frederick L. Fuller
By
Philipp Phelps Sawyer
Attys

STILL intrigued with the possibilities of improving the computing scale, Mr. Fuller on September 14, 1897, filed an application for a patent in which he set forth the following purposes:

The invention relates to improvements in indicating mechanism designed particularly for application to weighing-scales for the purpose of indicating the price or total cost of articles weighed, it being the object of the present invention to provide mechanism of this character which shall be of simple and durable construction, having few parts, and which shall be reliable and accurate both in adjustment and in operation.

Broadly the invention consists in an indicating or like mechanism for application to price-scales and other machines comprising a rotary member and a member coacting therewith, one of said members being inclined, with its inclination varying progressively in a transverse direction, and one member being adjustable relatively to the other in such direction. When such mechanism is applied to a weighing-scale for the purpose of indicating the price of the article weighed, one of the two members will be mounted in the scale, so as to be moved relatively to the other member in accordance with the weight, so as to actuate the price-indicating devices.

F. L. FULLER.
INDICATING OR LIKE MECHANISM FOR PRICE SCALES.

No. 603,505.   Patented May 3, 1898.

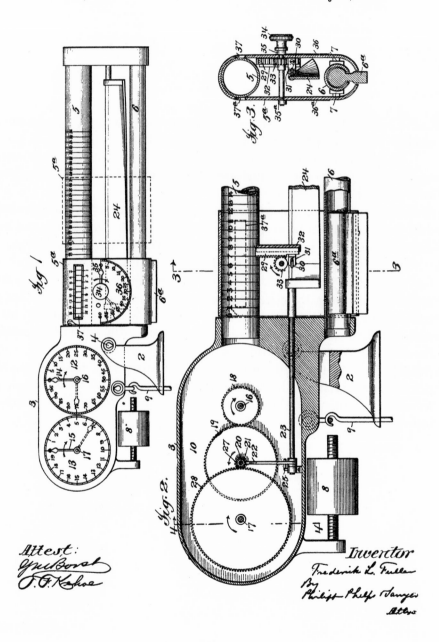

Attest:

Inventor
Frederick L. Fuller
By
Philipp Philp Sanger
Attys

*A*NOTHER scale improvement was filed for patent, also on September 14, 1897, with the following description:

This invention relates to improvements in indicating mechanism designed particularly for application to weighing-scales for the purpose of indicating the price or total cost of articles weighed, it being the object of the present invention to provide mechanism of this character which shall be of simple and durable construction, having few parts, and which shall be reliable and accurate both in adjustment and in operation.

Broadly the invention consists in an indicating or like mechanism for application to price-scales and other machines comprising a rotary member consisting of a pivoted wing having an inclined face for controlling the extent of its operation and an actuator therefor, one of said members, preferably the actuator, being adjustable transversely to the other and the inclination of the rotary member or wing varying progressively in the direction of such adjustment to suit in the case of price-scales variations in the unit prices of the articles weighed, so as to secure actuation of the indicating mechanism in accordance with such unit price.

F. L. FULLER.
WEIGHING SCALE AND VALUE CALCULATING AND REGISTERING MECHANISM.
(Application filed Feb. 6, 1894. Renewed Nov. 10, 1898.)

(No Model.)   4 Sheets—Sheet 1

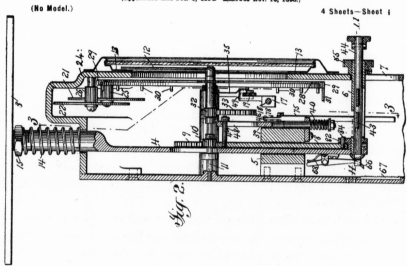

Fig. 2.

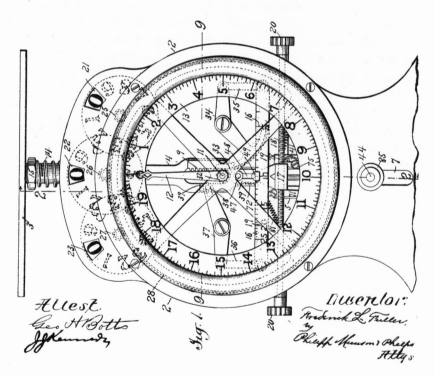

Fig. 1.

Attest.
Geo. H. Botts
J. J. Kennedy

Inventor:
Frederick L. Fuller,
by
Philipp, Munson & Phelps
Attys.

COMBINATION of weight and price—the basis of the computing scale—had certain disadvantages in the early days of this machine, and Mr. Fuller applied for another scale patent with the following explanation:

In the operation of this construction the article is first weighed, and then when the vibrations of the weighing mechanism have ceased the latter is locked against further movement. The calculating mechanism, being first set or adjusted for operation in accordance with the unit price of the article, is then released and operated by its actuating mechanism and in turn operates the registering mechanism. The movement of the calculating mechanism continues until the stop mechanism referred to controlled by the weighing mechanism engages and arrests it. The calculating mechanism will preferably include indicators, and the setting mechanism will preferably act in conjunction with a scale indicating units of price, so as to indicate the price. With such indicators upon the completion of the operation as just described there will be exhibited the weight of the article, its price per pound or other unit, and its total value, which latter will also be transferred to the registering mechanism.

The separation of the operations of weighing and calculating and registering, as described, is of importance, as calculating and registering mechanisms thus operated are not affected by vibrations of the weighing mechanism, each of which would operate the registering mechanism and produce overregistration.

No. 655,899.

F. L. FULLER.
PRICE SCALE.
(Application filed Sept. 15, 1899. Renewed June 15, 1900.)

Patented Aug. 14, 1900.

(No Model.)

2 Sheets—Sheet 1

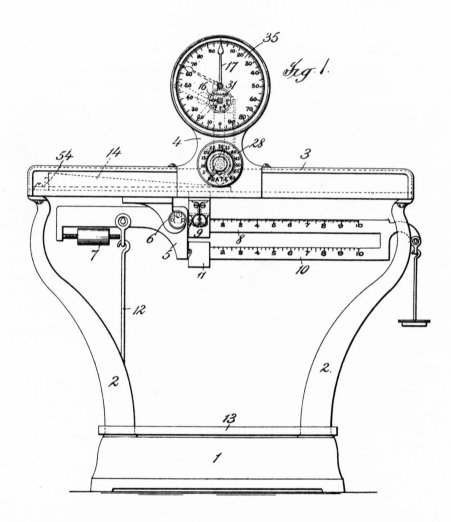

Fig. 1.

A NEW principle in computing scales was covered in a patent applied for by Mr. Fuller after a full year of work on one feature, which he had been assured by professors of mathematics was "impossible". This computing beam scale operating on a hyperbolic paraboliod, was described in the application as follows:

This invention relates to improvements in the computing or indicating mechanism of my prior Letters Patent, dated May 3, 1898, the object of the present invention, generally stated, being to adapt the inclined controlling member or actuator of said Letters Patent to weighing-scales of the type commonly known as "beam-scales."

F. L. FULLER.
CASH REGISTER.
APPLICATION FILED OCT. 14, 1904.

915,090.

Patented Mar. 16, 1909.
11 SHEETS—SHEET 1.

Fig.1

*I*N 1904, when he was manufacturing cash registers on his own, Mr. Fuller added an improvement which provided a printed record of cash or charge transactions and supplied the customer with a printed receipt. This was described in his patent application as follows:

With these mechanisms there are combined, among other things, registering mechanism for totalizing the amounts of the transactions, printing wheels by which the several transactions are printed on a strip of paper, and also a lever for restoring the indicators and printing wheels after one operation to their normal or zero positions before the next operation of the machine and which also serves to put under tension a spring operating, among other things, a printing platen, a drawer-lock and a gong, and also operating a member held in normal position by a detent controlled by the special key aforesaid and which member controls the operation of a shutter mechanism, and when moved by said spring from normal position prevents withdrawal or reoperation of said special key (and therefore reoperation of the machine) until this member, the indicating wheels and printing wheels are returned to normal or zero position.

F. L. FULLER.

ADDING MECHANISM FOR CASH REGISTERS, &c.

APPLICATION FILED FEB. 5, 1907. RENEWED APR. 9, 1909.

981,633.

Patented Jan. 17, 1911

4 SHEETS—SHEET 1.

Fig. 1.

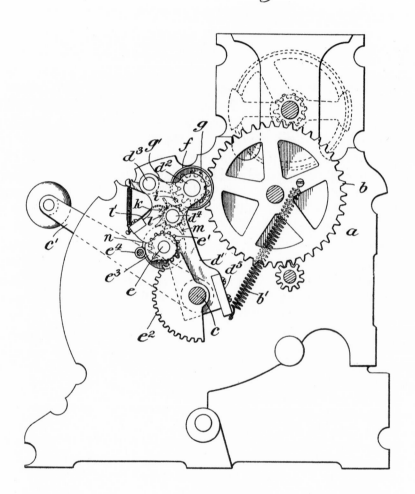

IN 1911, when he was chief inventor for the largest manufacturers of cash registers in the world, Mr. Fuller's efforts to improve the adding mechanism in this device resulted in a patent application in which he described his invention as follows:

This invention relates to adding mechanisms for cash registers and the like and has for its object to produce a mechanism of this character which shall be both positive and definite in action, without liability to overthrow of any of the adding wheels, while at the same time the totalizer shall be simple in construction and easily applied to and removed from the cash register or other machine in connection with which it is employed.

In accordance with the invention the totalizer or adding mechanism is moved into driving engagement with the main driving gears of the register or other machine and is moved out of engagement therewith during the carrying or advance of each number wheel or disk one step or number through the completion of the rotation of the wheel of next lower denomination.

F. L. FULLER.

CASH REGISTER.

APPLICATION FILED DEC. 31, 1897.

1,003,732.

Patented Sept. 19, 1911.

8 SHEETS—SHEET 1.

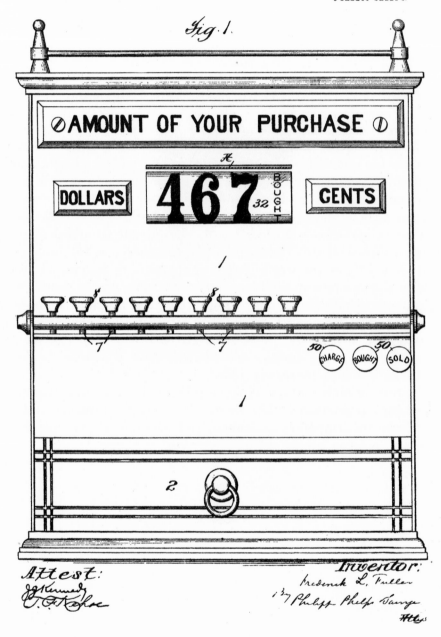

Fig. 1.

*A*LSO in 1911, Mr. Fuller was granted a patent on a cash register fifteen years after the filing of the application. This covered an improved method of printing the sales check, as described:

This invention relates to certain novel and useful improvements in machines for indicating sales and printing and adding checks, and has for its objects to provide a machine which shall temporarily indicate and permanently register the amount of each sale, which shall make for each such sale a check showing the amount of said sale, which shall also imprint upon said check in addition to the amount an additional word or sign which shall still further identify the check, as for instance the word "Bought", or the word "Sold", or the word "Charged". I also include in this machine in addition to the foregoing one or more totalizing registers which shall totalize respectively the amounts representing the aggregate of the checks bearing each of the distinguishing marks just referred to, that is to say, all sales charged shall be added together upon one of the totalizing devices, and likewise those which are bought or sold for cash will be separately added.

A further object is to make each printed check in duplicate whereof one copy is retained within the machine and the printing upon said copy forms the temporary indication, and the other is given to the customer and is taken by the cashier or retained as a memorandum.

F. L. FULLER.

TOTAL PRINTING CASH REGISTER.

APPLICATION FILED JUNE 6, 1910.

1,022,230.

Patented Apr. 2, 1912.

3 SHEETS—SHEET 2.

FIG.2.

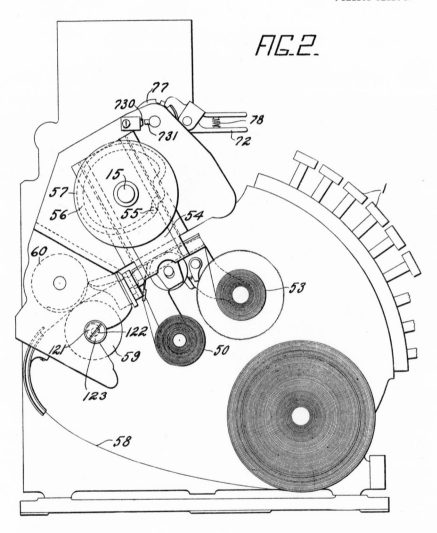

*A*N INVENTION which was destined to outgrow in a startling manner the original purpose for which it was intended, was patented by Mr. Fuller in 1912. Known as the total-printing cash register, its principle has since been embodied in accounting machines and other devices demanding speed and mathematical accuracy. In his patent application Mr. Fuller described this invention as follows:

This invention relates to accounting machines and more particularly to the printing mechanism thereof, and its principal object is to provide improved mechanism for printing totals as well as items upon a record strip.

Another object of this invention is to provide an interlocking mechanism between the manipulative devices which control the positioning of the item type carriers, and the mechanism for recording the total, so as to prevent the operation of the total recording mechanism when the item manipulative devices are operated, and to prevent the operation of the item manipulative devices when the total recording mechanism is positioned to record the total of the items.

Another object of this invention is to compel the disabling of the check strip feeding mechanism as an incident to the recording of the total.

Another object of this invention is to provide an improved form of inking mechanism for the type carriers.

1,088,068.

Fig.1.

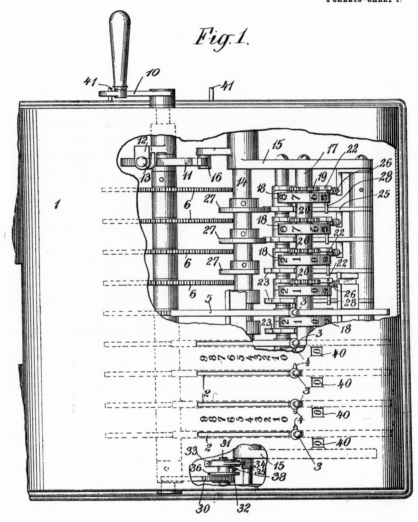

*A*S THE use of adding mechanisms was being extended rapidly in all sorts of cash registers, accounting machines, etc., Mr. Fuller devoted a great deal of time and research to possibilities of their improvement. One such improvement, for which letters patent were issued in 1914, described the purpose of the device briefly as follows:

My invention relates to adding mechanisms, such as are used in calculating machines, cash registers, and analogous constructions, and has for its object the production of a simple and positively operated mechanism, adapted to the addition of selected numerals.

In the accompanying drawings, forming a part of this specification, I have illustrated my adding mechanism or counter in connection with sufficient means to operate the same. Such illustrations as I have given show that part of an ordinary adding machine embodying my construction, which is sufficient to fully illustrate my invention, but without the inclusion of other parts of such a machine which are commonly used to indicate and register or record the results of the operation of the mechanism.

F. L. FULLER.
MULTIPLE CASH REGISTER.
APPLICATION FILED DEC. 6, 1910.

1,117,179.

Patented Nov. 17, 1914.
16 SHEETS—SHEET 16

FIG. 22.

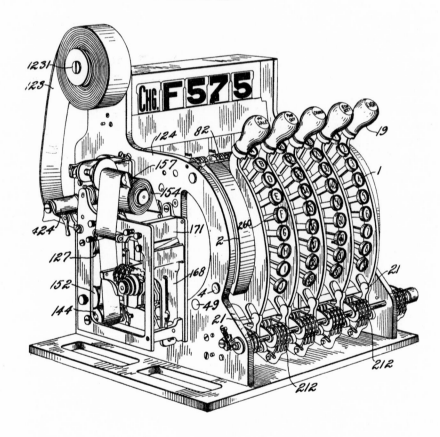

A CASH register radically different from all others was described and patented by Mr. Fuller under the title of the multiple cash register, described in the patent application as follows:

This invention relates to cash registers accomplishing the usual functions of multiple totalizer cash registers, namely in totalizing according to classes the different transactions entered in the register, in making printed records of transactions and temporarily indicating similar data concerning each transaction. It differs from other two-motion cash registers, that is, registers, which to operate, first require manipulation of amount and special setting devices such as transaction keys and then the operation of driving mechanism, in construction and in an arrangement whereby class of transaction selecting devices also serve for the application of driving power to the machine, having for its object the saving of one manual operation for each entered transaction. It is customary in two-motion cash registers to have a set of amount determining and a set of transaction determining devices and a single device for transmitting power, such as a crank lever or motor of some kind.

This invention provides a cash register with a plurality of such power devices, each of which also acts as a transaction determining device.

F. L. FULLER.
CHANGE INDICATING CASH REGISTER.
APPLICATION FILED DEC. 7, 1910.

1,122,489.

Patented Dec. 29, 1914.
4 SHEETS—SHEET 1

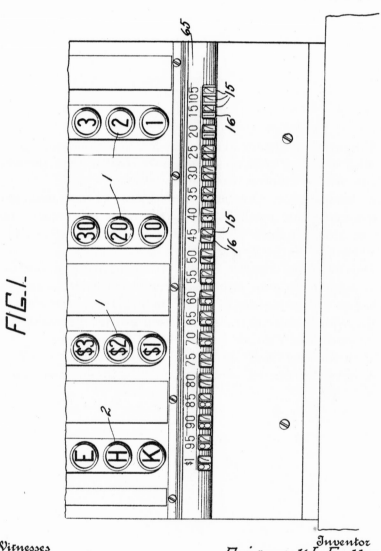

FIG. 1.

Witnesses
P. W. Fairchild
J. B. Ricketts

Inventor
Frederick L. Fuller
W. E. Murphy
and R. Chase
Attorneys

*T*HE figuring of change due on a cash transaction, when the customer pays with a bill or coin of larger denomination than the total of his purchase always involves the human element—unless it can be controlled mechanically. One clerk will figure change with more speed and accuracy than another, and to eliminate this human factor Mr. Fuller in 1914 obtained a patent on a change indicating cash register. His application set forth that:

This invention relates to accounting mechanisms, and among its objects is to provide an improved accounting device, herein shown as attached to a cash register of a well known type, and adapted to indicate the change due in transactions entered in the register, requiring little space and of a simple and improved construction.

With this and incidental objects in view, the invention consists in certain novel features of construction and combinations of parts.

F. L. FULLER.
CALCULATING MECHANISM.
APPLICATION FILED AUG. 13, 1909.

1,151,677.

Patented Aug. 31, 1915.
10 SHEETS—SHEET 3.

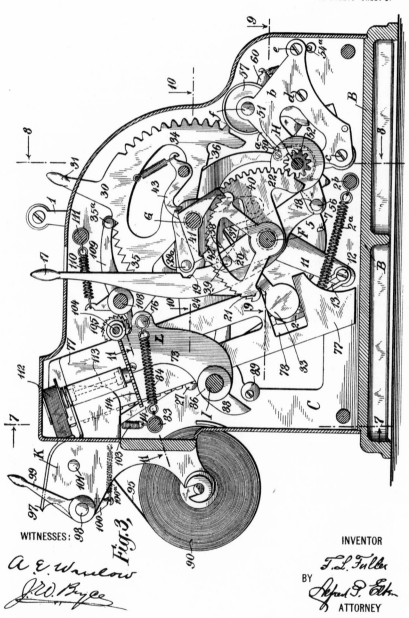

Fig.3

WITNESSES:

A. E. Winslow

J. W. Bryce

INVENTOR

F. L. Fuller

BY

ATTORNEY

*A*NOTHER calculating mechanism, designed to perform its functions with greater simplicity than the then existing devices, was patented by Mr. Fuller in 1915, the application for the patent having stated that:

My invention relates to calculating mechanism, and has for its object the production of a simple mechanism which can be readily operated to add and tabulate numbers and their sums.

1,161,042.

FIG. 2.

FIG. 1.

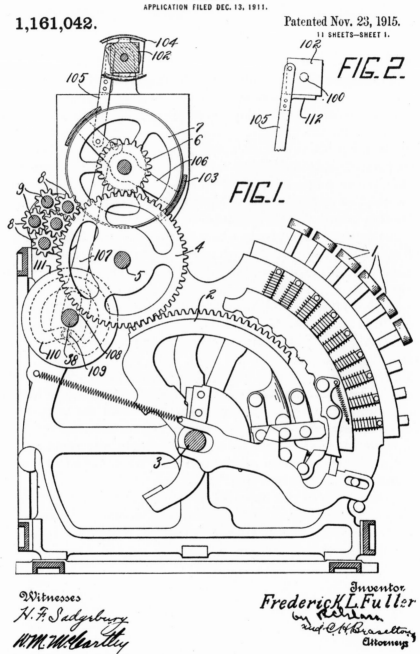

CONSTANTLY working to improve both the construction and operation of cash registers, Mr. Fuller on November 23, 1915, obtained a patent on new features described in the application as follows:

This invention relates to improvements in accounting machines and one of the objects thereof is to provide such a type of machine with a pluralty of independent accumulators any one of which may be brought into cooperative relation with a set of actuators, these actuators also being adapted to cooperate with a grand accumulator, which accumulates the total of several of the independent accumulators.

Another object of this invention is to provide mechanism for disabling the grand accumulator when certain of the independent accumulators are brought into cooperative relation with the actuators.

Another object of this invention is to provide transfer devices which are common to the independent and the grand accumulators.

A further object of this invention is to provide an improved form of operating mechanism for the indicators whereby said indicators are moved directly from one position to another without returning to their normal starting position.

A further object of this invention is to provide a special bank of keys with suitable locking mechanism therefor, so constructed that when certain accumulators are in cooperative relation with the actuators, the key corresponding in designation to the selected accumulator will be unlocked, while when other accumulators are brought into cooperative relation with the actuators all of the said keys are unlocked so that any one of the same may be operated.

Another object of this invention is to provide a movable frame carrying record material upon which are entered, written and printed data, the said frame being moved from one position to another to have the different data entered thereupon.

W. H. MUZZY & F. L. FULLER.
ATTACHMENT FOR CASH REGISTERS.
APPLICATION FILED FEB. 20, 1911.

1,161,069.

Patented Nov. 23, 1915.
4 SHEETS—SHEET 1.

FIG. 1.

A COMBINATION of the cash register and a filing cabinet, which would compel the completion of certain transactions down to filing before another transaction could be started, was provided for in an ingenious device patented by Mr. Fuller in 1915. The description embodied in the patent application stated:

When the accounting machine is operated for the purpose of entering "charge" or "received on account" transactions therein, the machine is automatically locked at the end of the operation and remains in such condition until the filing cabinet is operated, which operation will automatically release the accounting machine. In the entering of "cash" and "paid out" transactions the above mentioned locking mechanism for the accounting machine is not brought into play, therefore permitting successive operations of the machine without an intervening operation of the filing cabinet. In the specific embodiment of the invention, the arrangement described is very desirable, as frequently in an establishment where the two devices or machines are in use, a clerk after making a "charge" transaction or receiving cash on account, may make the proper entries upon the loose leaf system which is in universal use and then deposit the leaf or slip in the filing cabinet without making the proper entry in the accounting machine. With the described invention in use this is impossible, as the slip receptacle or filing cabinet remains locked until either a "received on account" or a "charge" transaction is entered in the accounting machine.

F. L. FULLER.
INDICATING MECHANISM.
APPLICATION FILED MAR. 18, 1914.

1,163,748.

Patented Dec. 14, 1915.
4 SHEETS—SHEET 1.

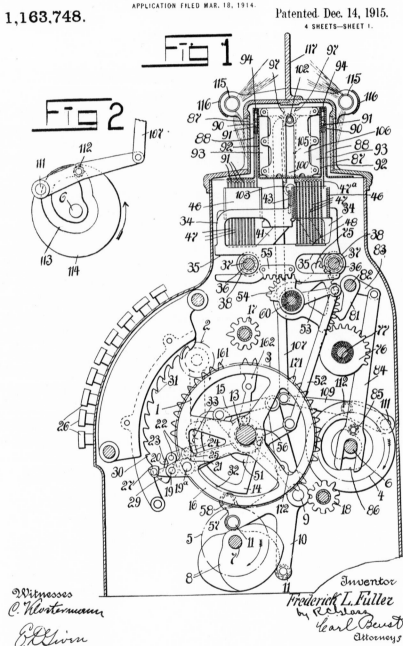

FIG 1

FIG 2

SETTING forth objections to existing types of both tablet and roller indicators as used on a cash register, Mr. Fuller on December 11, 1915, received a patent on an improved indicating mechanism which he described in part as follows:

The object of the invention is to provide an improved indication combining the advantages of the two best types of indicators, the tablet and the roller, without the disadvantages of either. Roller indicators have the advantage of permitting a compact grouping of the indicia for a bank or denominational section of the machine, but, owing to the curved surface carrying the characters, the upper and lower parts of said characters do not stand out as clearly as is desirable. The principal objection, however, is that because of the limited surface available on the peripheries of such indicators, unless the indicators are made unreasonably large in diameter, the characters must necessarily be small and are not, therefore, easily read except from a position near the machine. Tablet indicators are not open to these objections, as they always present a plane surface to the eye, and the extent of surface on each can readily be made great enough to permit making the characters of such size that they may be read from any reasonable distance.

F. L. FULLER.
CASH REGISTER.
APPLICATION FILED AUG. 22, 1913.

1,182,999.

Patented May 16, 1916.
4 SHEETS—SHEET 3.

Fig. 4.

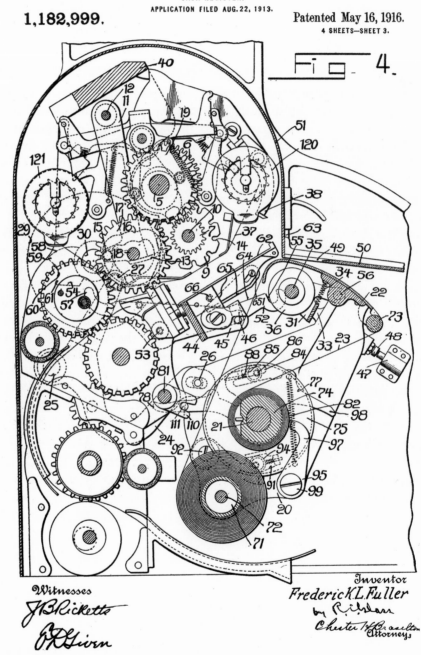

Witnesses

JB Ricketts

Inventor
Frederic K. L. Fuller
by
Chester H. Croselton
Attorneys

A DEVICE which made possible the entry of written information on the printed cash slip of cash registers was patented by Mr. Fuller on May 16, 1916. The application set forth the following information:

Described in general terms the invention comprises an improved mechanism for printing on a record strip designed to receive both written and printed records. Such a printer is generally known as an autographic printer and the strip is usually called an autographic strip, and these are the terms used in this specification. A movable frame for carrying the autographic strip is provided, this frame being normally in position for the strip to receive the written record, and, upon every operation of the machine, it will be oscillated to the position for the strip to receive an impression from the type carriers after which the frame is returned to normal position. The strip is spaced during the return of the table to normal position. When entering cash transactions or other transactions where no written record is needed, the items may be single spaced thereby preventing unnecessary waste of the record paper. However, these single spaces are so narrow that there is not enough room opposite the printed items to make satisfactory written records, particularly where several successive entries are printed each requiring a written notation. A manipulative device is therefore provided for controlling the paper feeding mechanism so that the strip may be double spaced between the printed items when making entries requiring a written record or explanation, and single spaced between cash and other items requiring no such notations.

F. L. FULLER.
DIFFERENTIAL MECHANISM FOR ACCOUNTING MACHINES.
APPLICATION FILED OCT. 1, 1913.

1,195,198.

Patented Aug. 22, 1916.
8 SHEETS—SHEET 1.

FIG.1.

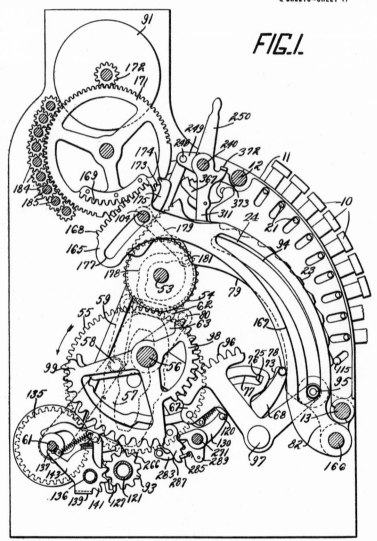

Witnesses
Harry W. Lindsey Jr.
H. F. Sadgebury

Inventor
Frederick L. Fuller
by R. Chton
Chester H. Braselton
Attorneys

*L*ESSENING of strains, through smoother mechanical action, is always the goal of designers of accounting machines, cash registers and other machines in which the operating impulse is accompanied by shock. Longer life for such a machine, and better performance when in use were the object of the differential mechanism patented by Mr. Fuller on August 22, 1916. The description on which this patent was granted said in part:

One of the principal objects of this invention is to obtain a better form of key controlled differential mechanism, which subjects the machine to less jars than the known forms and the operation of which is much smoother in action. To this end the mechanism shown in the illustrative form disclosed herein is constructed to rotate an accounting device and the actuators therefor during a predetermined period regardless of the extent of rotation and to regulate the speed of such rotation as desired.

F. L. FULLER.
AUTOGRAPHIC REGISTER.
APPLICATION FILED JULY 19, 1913.

1,202,825

Patented Oct. 31, 1916.
4 SHEETS—SHEET 1.

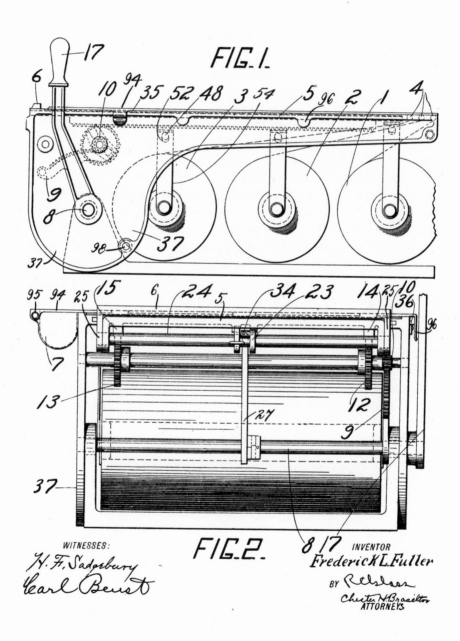

FIG.1.

FIG.2.

WITNESSES:
H. F. Sadgsbury
Carl Benst

INVENTOR
Frederick L. Fuller
BY Relslaer
Chester H. Braselton
ATTORNEYS

*A*N IMPROVED and more flexible feeding device for an autographic cash register was patented by Mr. Fuller on October 31, 1916. The application on which this patent was granted said in part:

A large number of autographic devices have been designed heretofore employing various forms of feeding devices, but it is one of the objects of the present invention to provide an improved form of feeding device and particularly a feeding device which is adapted to handle large sized record strips.

In autographic machines employing feeding devices heretofore designed it was found practically impossible to feed a plurality of record strips, all of which had previously been printed and to feed the strips simultaneously so as to cause the printed forms on the various strips to register properly to permit of a perfect record being made on the several strips. In many well known devices of this type a written record is made on the original or top strip of a series and this record is transferred to any desired number of duplicate strips placed beneath the original record strip and having transfer paper or other transfer material interposed between the various strips. Many well known forms of feeding devices are satisfactory where the duplicate and triplicate strips are merely in a blank form, but where it is desired to have the duplicate and triplicate strips printed with the same form as the original strip, it is found very difficult to provide a feeding mechanism capable of giving an exactly equal feed to all of the plurality of strips.

The principal object of the present invention is to provide an efficient feeding device for giving an equal feed to a number of previously printed record strips.

F. L. FULLER.
CASH REGISTER.
APPLICATION FILED DEC. 21, 1914.

1,242,170.

Patented Oct. 9, 1917.
19 SHEETS—SHEET 19.

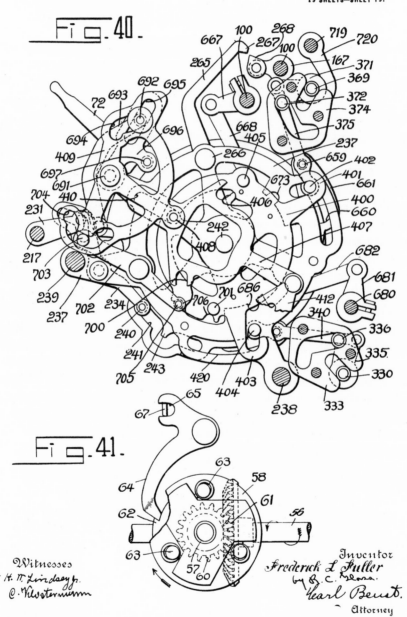

Fig. 40.

Fig. 41.

Inventor
Frederick L. Fuller
by R. C. Elona.
Earl Beust.
Attorney

*T*HE scope of the cash register was greatly widened by an invention on which Mr. Fuller was granted a patent on October 9, 1917. Setting forth the extended uses made possible by this invention the application for patent stated:

The principal object of this invention is to design a machine adapted more particularly for use in hotels, restaurants and the like. The machine embodies a plurality of individual totalizers for segregating the totals of the different classes of provisions sold and a grand totalizer for accumulating the difference between the grand total of these individual totalizers and the total of provisions returned, a separate totalizer being provided to accumulate the value of the provisions returned.

A further object of this invention is to provide an improved mechanism for controlling total and subtotal operations of machines having a plurality of totalizers.

Another object of the invention is to provide novel means for releasing the operating mechanism so as to compel a conjoint operation of a plurality of keys in an adding operation, this means being constructed to release the operating mechanism upon movement of the device, controlling total and subtotal printing operations, to one of its positions, preparing the machine for printing a total or subtotal from the grand totalizer, or by the conjoint operation of a key and the device to one of its positions preparing the machine for printing a total or subtotal from a transaction totalizer.

1,253,367.

Patented Jan. 15, 1918.

5 SHEETS—SHEET 1.

FIG.1

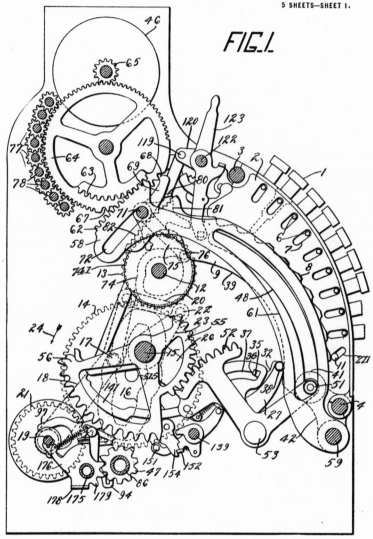

Inventor
Frederick L. Fuller
by R Chilson.
Chester H Braselton
Attorneys

Witnesses
H. W. Lindsey Jr.
H. F. Sadgebury

*S*PEED and accuracy in mechanical operation were always Mr. Fuller's guiding stars as he proceeded with his task of perfecting cash registers. Accordingly, in an application for a patent on a transfer mechanism for accounting machines, he set forth that:

The principal object of this invention is to provide a simple and efficient transfer mechanism, one so constructed as to require less time for effecting transfers than is required in the usual forms of transfer mechanism. The saving of time is of considerable importance in highly developed machines of this class which, among other functions, may be adapted to accumulate and indicate amounts and to record the items indicated and the totals accumulated on a detail strip, an inserted sales slip, and checks issued by the machine. Care must be taken to give the proper time for the accomplishment of each of these objects, all of the parts being so operated during one complete rotation of the main drive or cam shaft.

F. L. FULLER.
CASH REGISTER.
APPLICATION FILED JULY 10, 1915.

1,301,678.

Patented Apr. 22, 1919.
10 SHEETS—SHEET 4.

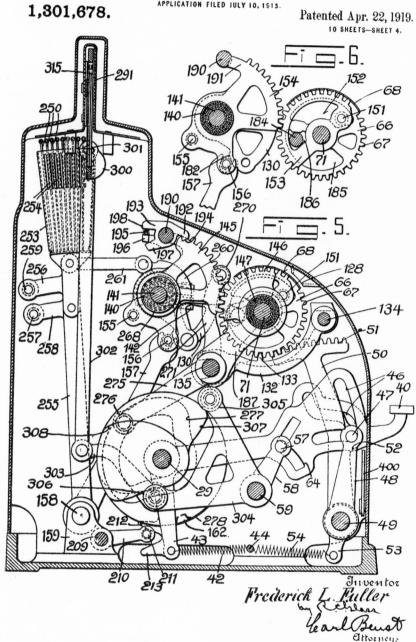

Inventor
Frederick L. Fuller
Earl Benst
Attorneys

A SIMPLIFICATION and general improvement of the ten key cash register and accounting machine was perfected by Mr. Fuller in 1915, when a patent was applied for that was granted on April 22, 1919. The application describing this machine said in part:

It is usual in accounting machines of the various types to provide manipulative amount determining means for controlling the amount differential mechanism of the machine and special manipulative means for controlling the indicating or recording of special characters to identify the clerk making each transaction, the class of each transaction, etc. Special and separate manipulative means are also employed in some accounting machines for controlling the selection of individual totalizers or counters for operation or for disabling the totalizer engaging mechanism on certain operations.

It is the principal object of this invention to construct a machine so that common manipulative means serve to accomplish the different functions of a plurality of manipulative means of different classes, heretofore employed. In the present form of embodiment disclosed herein one series of keys is employed to perform the functions previously performed by two or more adjustable levers or series of keys of different classes, thus reducing the space required by a plurality of levers or series of keys as well as simplifying the construction and operation of the machine.

It is thought that the present invention is the first in the art to provide a machine employing a series of keys each key being used to accomplish the different functions formerly accomplished by separate keys or levers.

F. L. FULLER.
REGISTERING AND RECORDING MECHANISM.
APPLICATION FILED SEPT. 2, 1915.

1,311,884.

Patented Aug. 5, 1919.
15 SHEETS—SHEET 1.

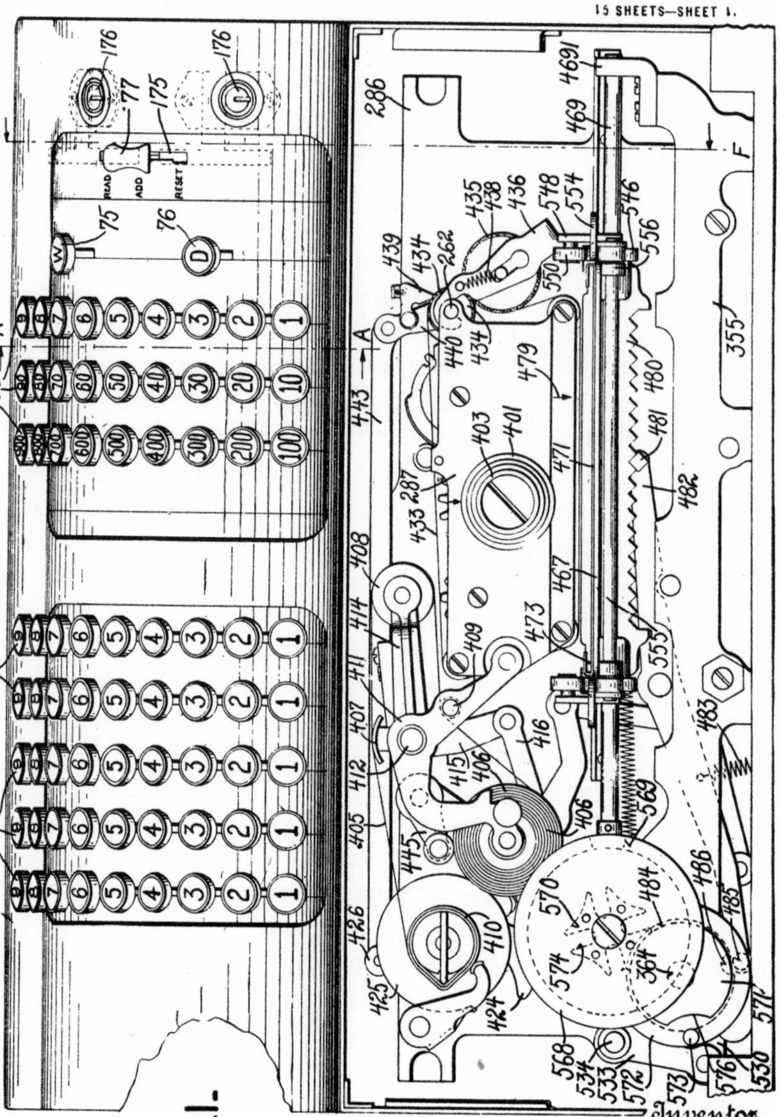

FIG. 1.

Inventor
Frederick L. Fuller
by
Carl Beust
Attorneys

A MARKED widening of the scope of printing cash registers, i.e., those that printed on a continuous tape and on individual sales checks, was accomplished by Mr. Fuller after extended research and experiment, and patented on August 5, 1919. Describing the improvements covered by this patent, the application stated:

The principal object of this invention is to provide an improved form of printing mechanism.

Another object of this invention is to provide a machine with a plurality of totalizers and construct improved printing means for printing in columns appropriate to the totalizers.

It is also an object of this invention to provide improved means for shifting the type carriers for the purpose of columnar printing instead of shifting the record material.

The invention also comprises a carriage for holding a card and a depositor's book and means for removing the card after an item has been printed thereon, to permit the item to be printed on the book, the latter being under the card at the beginning of the operation of the machine. The impression means is operated twice to carry the card against the type carriers the first time and the book against the carriers the second time.

Improved means for preventing the contact of the impression means with the type carriers when no record material is present is also embodied in the present invention.

The invention also discloses novel means for preventing operation of the machine when the record strip is exhausted.

A still further object of the invention is to provide an improved form of zero eliminating mechanism having the well known function of preventing the printing of zeros by the type carriers of higher order than that adjusted to print another amount character and permitting the printing of zeros by those type carriers of lower order when one of higher order is adjusted to print an amount character other than zero.

F. L. FULLER.

CASH REGISTER.

APPLICATION FILED JUNE 27, 1918.

1,336,693.

Patented Apr. 13, 1920.

5 SHEETS—SHEET 1.

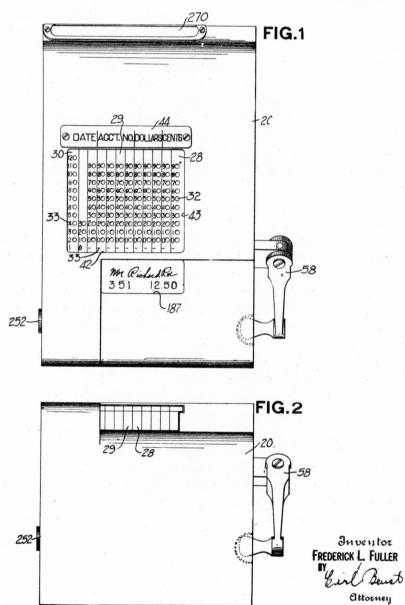

FIG.1

FIG.2

Inventor

FREDERICK L. FULLER

BY

Earl Beust

Attorney

$\mathcal{A}$N IMPROVED portable cash register was patented by Mr. Fuller in 1920—and the application for the patent set forth its purpose and probable uses as follows:

This invention relates to improvements in cash registers and the like, the primary object being to devise a mechanism which is adapted to be transported from place to place by the operator, thereby making it very adaptable for use among ice men, milk men, expressmen, insurance collectors, and in fact collectors of every description. The machine is designed to be closed up as much as possible so that dust, dirt, water, etc., will be kept out of the mechanism, because it may be subjected to all kinds of weather and all sorts of other conditions when being used by collectors and others heretofore mentioned.

The present machine is designed to register amounts and issue checks commensurate with these amounts.

Another object of the present improvement is to provide the machine with a record strip, and a device cooperating therewith, whereby the same is adapted to receive autographic notations. Being thus provided with a check issuing device and a record strip, the machine affords protection to the customer or payer and also to the proprietor or manager of the business. The check is given to the customer as a receipt, and the record strip receives an impression identical to that printed on the issued check so that the proprietor is provided with a printed record of every transaction that has taken place.

The present invention differs from a former machine, invented by the applicant and disclosed in a pending application Serial No. 220,752 filed March 6, 1918, in that, the present mechanism is provided with an autographic device while the mechanism in the application referred to does not have such autographic feature. The present machine is also provided with a plurality of printing mechanisms, whereas the mechanism in the application above referred to is provided with only one printing mechanism.

F. L. FULLER.
MULTIPLE TICKET ISSUING REGISTER.
APPLICATION FILED APR. 2, 1917.

1,340,221.

Patented May 18, 1920.
13 SHEETS—SHEET 1.

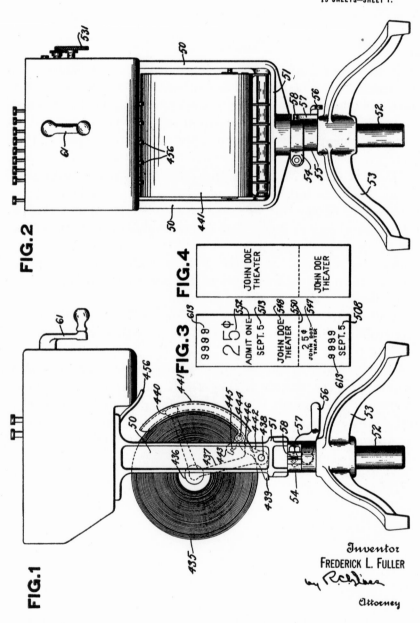

FIG.2

FIG.4

FIG.3

FIG.1

JOHN DOE THEATER

JOHN DOE THEATER

9998 25¢ ADMIT ONE SEPT. 5 JOHN DOE THEATER 25¢ JOHN DOE THEATER 9899 SEPT. 5

Inventor
FREDERICK L. FULLER

Attorney

*T*HE growing use of cash registers in all kinds of businesses had created a demand for a machine issuing numerous cash receipts, tickets, etc. To meet this demand Mr. Fuller designed a multiple-ticket-issuing register on which he was granted a patent on May 18, 1920. The description of this invention in the patent application filed April 2, 1917, said in part:

This invention relates to improvements in ticket issuing and accounting machines and has particular reference to machines of the kind constructed to be variably operated to issue one or more tickets of several different classes or prices and add the value of each ticket on a totalizer as the ticket is issued.

One object of the invention is to provide a simple compact machine for use in the ticket offices of theaters and in other places where several different classes of tickets are used.

Another object of the invention is to provide improved mechanism for controlling the variable operation of the machine according to the number of tickets to be issued.

Another object of the invention is to provide improved mechanism for numbering the tickets as they are issued. In the form shown this mechanism is constructed so that it may be prepared to number all the tickets according to a single series of consecutive numbers or to number the tickets of each class according to a series of consecutive numbers peculiar to its class only.

F. L. FULLER.
CASH REGISTER.
APPLICATION FILED MAR. 6, 1918.

1,369,415.

Patented Feb. 22, 1921.
5 SHEETS—SHEET 1.

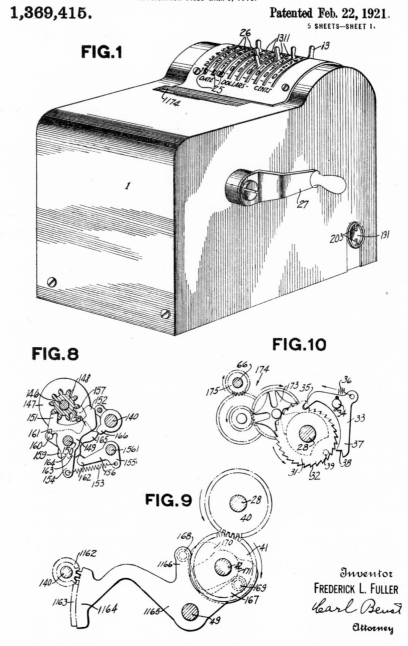

FIG.1

FIG.8

FIG.10

FIG.9

Inventor
FREDERICK L. FULLER
Carl Berst
Attorney

ON MARCH 6, 1918, Mr. Fuller filed an application for a portable cash register. Another application for a similar machine, with improvements, was filed on June 27, 1918, and the patent on the latter was granted on April 13, 1920. Nearly a year later, on February 22, 1921, the original application resulted in the granting of another patent. The description of the device said:

This invention relates to improvements in cash registers, the primary object being to devise such a mechanism which is adapted to be transported from place to place by the operator.

The present machine is designed to register amounts and issue checks printed commensurate with these amounts, the checks being issued as receipts, and is small enough to be readily carried in a case having a supporting strap slung over the shoulder of the operator.

The register is provided with a detail strip and due to its portable capability is well adapted for use by ice, milk, newspaper, gas and electricity bill collectors and in fact by collectors of all sorts since the machine is a safeguard for the employer of the collector due to the printed record and also for the payer furnishing him with a receipt.

F. L. FULLER.
MACHINE FOR PRINTING AND ISSUING RAILWAY TICKETS.
APPLICATION FILED OCT. 27, 1916.

1,382,637.

Patented June 28, 1921.
23 SHEETS—SHEET 1.

FIG.1

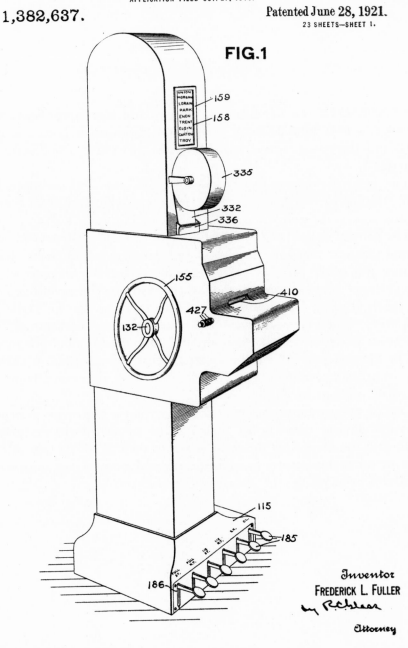

Inventor
FREDERICK L. FULLER
by R.C.Mear
Attorney

To EXPEDITE the handling of railway and steamship ticket sales Mr. Fuller in 1916 applied for a patent on a machine to print and issue tickets, and the patent was granted on June 28, 1921. The description said in part:

This invention relates to ticket issuing machines and has more particular relation to that class of ticket issuing machines adapted for use in issuing tickets for railroad and steamship lines or other analogous uses.

The general object of this invention is to provide an improved compact and efficient machine for use in ticket offices of railroads, steamship lines and other lines of travel to issue tickets of different classes and accurately account for the money received for the tickets of each class, (such as "Full fare round trip", "Full fare one way", "Half fare round trip", "Half fare one way", "Excursion" and "Clergyman") to each station as well as for the total amount received for all of the tickets issued by the machine. It will be apparent that the invention is capable of use in other embodiments without constituting departure from the scope of the present invention.

One of the principal objects of this invention is to provide improved destination devices constructed to print the names of the destination stations and the classes on the tickets, retain records of the number of tickets of each class issued to each station and control the numbering of and the printing of the values on the tickets.

F. L. FULLER.
MACHINE FOR PRINTING AND ISSUING RAILWAY TICKETS.
APPLICATION FILED DEC. 18, 1919.

1,392,929.

Patented Oct. 11, 1921.
19 SHEETS—SHEET 8

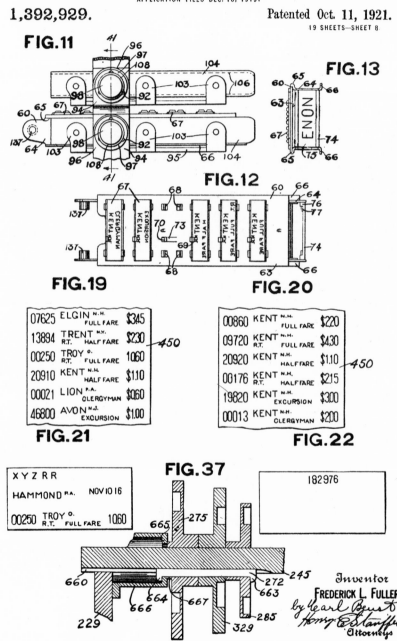

FIG.11

FIG.13

FIG.12

FIG.19

07625	ELGIN N.H. FULL FARE	$3.45
13894	TRENT N.Y. R.T. HALF FARE	$2.30
00250	TROY O. R.T. FULL FARE	10.60
20910	KENT N.H. HALF FARE	$1.10
00021	LION P.A. CLERGYMAN	$0.60
46800	AVON N.J. EXCURSION	$1.00

450

FIG.21

FIG.20

00860	KENT N.H. FULL FARE	$2.20
09720	KENT N.H. R.T. FULL FARE	$4.30
20920	KENT N.H. HALF FARE	$1.10
00176	KENT N.H. R.T. HALF FARE	$2.15
19820	KENT N.H. EXCURSION	$3.00
00013	KENT N.H. CLERGYMAN	$2.00

450

FIG.22

XYZRR

HAMMOND P.A.   NOV 10 16

00250 TROY O. R.T. FULL FARE 10.60

FIG.37

182976

Inventor
FREDERICK L. FULLER
by Carl Beust
Henry C. Stauffer
Attorneys

*I*N 1919, while his original application for a machine to print and issue railway tickets was pending, Mr. Fuller filed an application for an improvement, in which he said:

One of the principal objects of this invention is to provide improved destination devices constructed to print the names of the destination stations and the classes on the tickets, retain records of the number of tickets of each class issued to each station and control the numbering of and the printing of the values on the tickets. In the present embodiment but one destination device is provided for each station taken care of by the machine. Each destination device is adapted to print the name of the destination station, the classes of the tickets and any other desired information as well as control the printing of the number and value of the ticket of each particular class. In some inventions relating to railroad ticket machines one destination device is provided for each class of tickets to each station instead of for all classes of tickets to each station and therefore the number of desination devices is greatly increased. It is evident that in such inventions the destination devices require more space and their selection is more tedious and requires more time.

A further object of the invention is to provide improved means for selecting the desired destination devices for use and moving it into position to print a ticket of the desired class. In the illustrative form of embodiment the destination devices are carried on an endless chain, which is adjusted to move the desired destination device into position to be inserted into the printing mechanism. Then a foot pedal, appropriate to the desired class of ticket, is operated to move the selected device into the printing mechanism so that the ticket of the desired class is printed and issued.

F. L. FULLER.
CASH REGISTER.
APPLICATION FILED APR. 24, 1918.

1,394,256.

Patented Oct. 18, 1921.
28 SHEETS—SHEET 1.

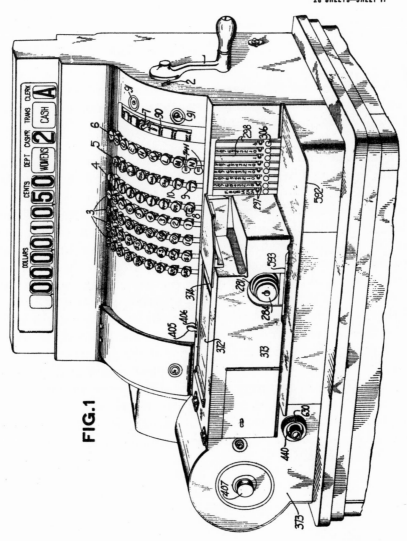

FIG.1

Inventor
FREDERICK L. FULLER
by Earl Beust
Attorney

A CASH register designed primarily for retail shoe stores was patented by Mr. Fuller on October 18, 1921. This was the result of a special study of the needs of establishments of this type. The application stated:

The machine embodies a plurality of individual totalizers for segregating the totals of different classes of goods sold and different classes of work done; a plurality of individual totalizers for segregating the totals of different classes of transactions; a plurality of individual totalizers for segregating the totals of sales by the various clerks; and a plurality of individual totalizers for segregating the amount of money received on account by the various cashiers. Although the present system contemplates and provides a means for segregating the amount of money received on account by the various cashiers, parts may be so arranged that other classes of transactions might be charged to the various cashiers in lieu of transactions where money was received on account without departing from the spirit and scope of the present improvement.

Another object of the present improvement is to provide a counter selecting mechanism cooperating with the differentials whereby various counters and combinations of counters may be selected and positioned for operation so that the amounts set up on the amount banks may be accumulated on any desired counter or accumulated on several desired counters simultaneously.

Aug. 12, 1924.

F. L. FULLER

CASH REGISTER

Filed May 7, 1918

1,504,226

13 Sheets-Sheet 2

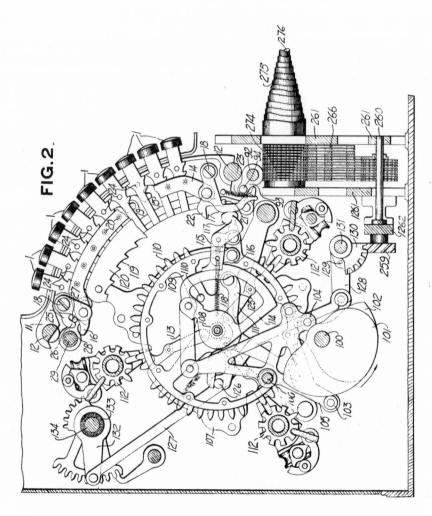

FIG.2.

*A*NOTHER of the many improvements in cash register printing mechanisms which Mr. Fuller designed was patented on August 12, 1924, with special reference to use in savings banks and similar institutions. The application for this patent set forth that:

The machine embodies a plurality of individual totalizers for segregating the totals of both deposited and withdrawal transactions handled by the different tellers; a plurality of individual totalizers for segregating the totals of different characters of negotiable papers or cash, making up a deposit; and an individual totalizer for segregating totals of interests, deposits and with drawal transactions.

A still further object of the present improvements is to construct one of the keys in a key bank so that it will only release the machine and not control the differential mechanism and to position an individual totalizer at the zero position of another key bank so that when no key in this bank is operated and the release key is depressed, the amount set up on the amount banks will be accumulated upon the totalizer which is located at the zero position of the said key bank.

The invention also comprises a shiftable carriage for holding a card or deposit slip and a depositor's book and improved means for removing the card or slip after an item has been printed thereon, to permit the item to be printed on the book, the latter being under the card or slip at the beginning of the operation of the machine. The impression means is operated twice to carry the card or slip against the type carrier the first time and the book against the carrier the second time. The paper carriage is shiftable so as to adjust the printing mediums to receive an impression at any desired point.

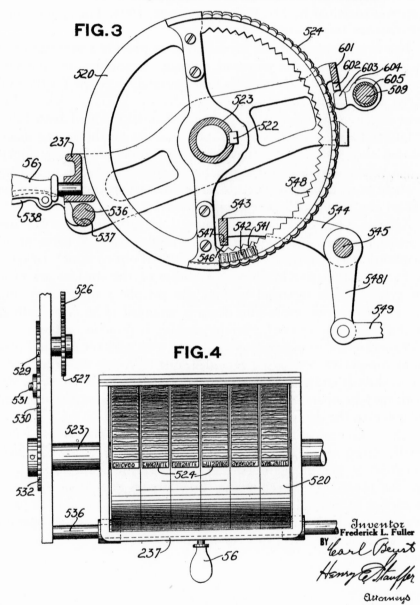

FIG.3

FIG.4

Inventor
Frederick L. Fuller
BY
Carl Beyst
Henry C. Stauffer
Attorneys

*S*TILL another improvement in the machine to print and issue railway tickets was patented by Mr. Fuller in August, 1924. The application for this patent set forth that:

The broad object of the invention is to provide a satisfactory machine for use in the ticket offices of railroads, steamship lines and similar places where it is necessary to issue and accurately account for the money received in payment for a number of different kinds of tickets. In the present instance the machine is constructed to take care of both full and half-fare tickets good between the station at which the issuing machine is located and each of a number of other stations. It will be apparent that the mechanism disclosed is capable of embodiment either in part or as a whole in machines designed to serve other purposes without departing from the broad spirit of the invention.

Another object of the invention is to provide improved means for printing upon tickets issued from a single strip the name or other information pertaining to any one of the stations to which tickets are sold. In the illustrative machine the names of the stations are printed from type carriers arranged around the periphery of a drum, in six rows of forty carriers each. This drum is arranged to be given both endwise and rotary movement, thereby making it possible to bring a type carrier in any row in position to cooperate with a ticket printing platen. Two manipulative devices are provided, one to rotate the drum and the other to shift it endwise. Either of these devices may be operated singly or both may be operated simultaneously depending upon the adjustment to be given to the drum.

After the station type carrying drum has been positioned, a device normally given an invariable extent of movement projects the selected type carrier to printing position and also locks the drum against movement. An invariably moved platen then presses the paper against the type carrier to print. One of the objects of the invention is to provide means for disabling the invariably moved platen in printing operations where it is not desired to print the name of a station.

FIG.2

FIG.3

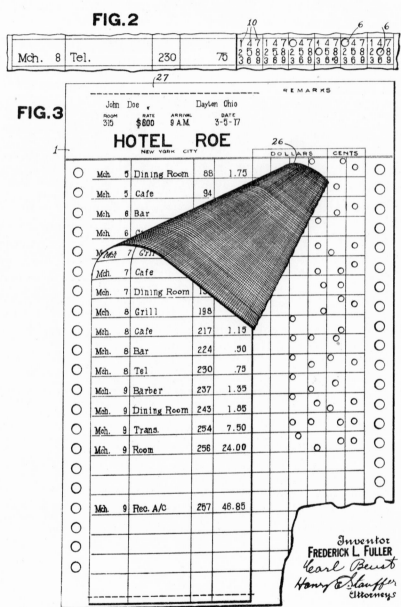

HOTEL ROE

Inventor
FREDERICK L. FULLER
Carl Beust
Henry E. Stauffer
Attorneys

A SIMPLE form of combined record sheet and customer's receipt for hotel use was patented by Mr. Fuller on September 9, 1924. Generally used in large hotels, the invention was described as follows:

This invention relates to improvements in a combined record sheet and receipt and has, among its objects, the provision of improved means for receiving thereon various items and the amount thereof in connection with a transaction extending frequently over several days, means for receiving an entry of said amounts so that the record sheet may be passed through a tabulating or sorting machine to keep summed up the current items following the entry of each item, an itemized receipt, exactly the same as the account at any time the transaction may be closed, upon which shall be finally entered the total amount.

F. L. FULLER

TICKET PRINTING MECHANISM

Filed March 23, 1916   24 Sheets-Sheet 7

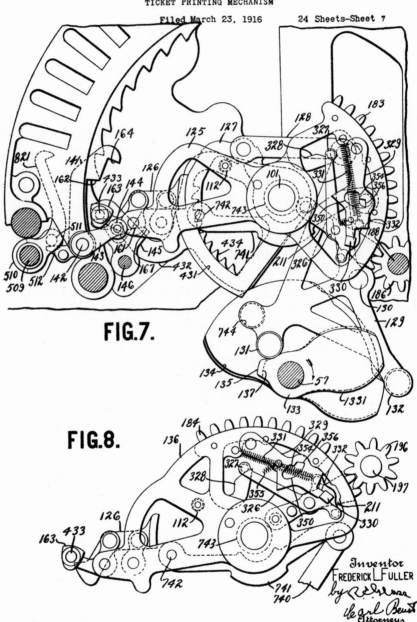

FIG.7.

FIG.8.

Inventor
FREDERICK L FULLER
by
Legal Beust
Attorneys

*T*HE ticket printing machine again engaged Mr. Fuller in research and experiment, which resulted in a much better arrangement for keeping records of total sales. The application described this result in the following language:

One of the further objects of the invention is to provide improved devices for retaining in the machine a record of the tickets sold to the various stations and numbering the tickets under the control of said devices as an incident to printing the tickets. In this embodiment these devices are shown as totalizers arranged in six groups of forty each, or two hundred and forty totalizers in all, this particular machine being designed to take care of ticket sales to that number of different stations. When the machine is operated to issue a ticket to a certain station the corresponding totalizer is first actuated to add one to the previous total in case the ticket is a half fare or two in case of a full fare and is then operated to control the setting of type carriers to print the new number or total on the ticket being issued. Both the adding and the type carrier controlling operations of the totalizer occur during the same operation of the driving mechanism.

July 27 , 1926.

F. L. FULLER

1,594,167

CASH REGISTER

Filed May 23, 1918

5 Sheets-Sheet 3

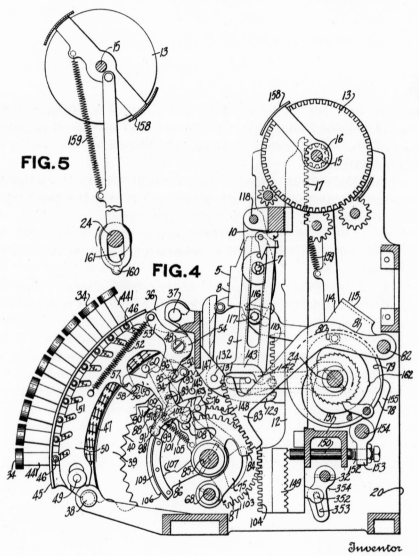

FIG.5

FIG.4

Inventor

FREDERICK L. FULLER

Carl Benst

Attorney

*K*EYBOARD control of cash registers having been found superior to setting levers, Mr. Fuller designed and patented a machine which had many advantages—simplicity of operation and ease of manufacture and assembly being prominent among them. The patent application on this register stated:

An object of the present improvement is to devise a novel form of keyboard construction which comprises but very few parts and which may be both rapidly manufactured and assembled.

Another object of the present improvement is to devise a novel form of differential mechanism cooperating with the novel keyboard above mentioned.

A further object is to provide the improved register with a bank of special transaction keys, a depression of one of which is necessary to release the machine, and to so combine with this key bank the totalizer control mechanism that when certain of the special transaction keys are depressed no amount will be accumulated on the totalizer even though an amount may be set up on the amount key banks.

A further object is to provide the special transaction key bank with a novel interlocking mechanism so associated with certain of the keys that it prevents a depression of two of such keys simultaneously.

A still further object of this invention is to provide a novel timing of the engagement of the totalizer mechanism and its actuating racks.

March 1, 1927.

F. L. FULLER ET AL

1,619,664

CASH REGISTER

Filed July 9. 1920

9 Sheets-Sheet 5

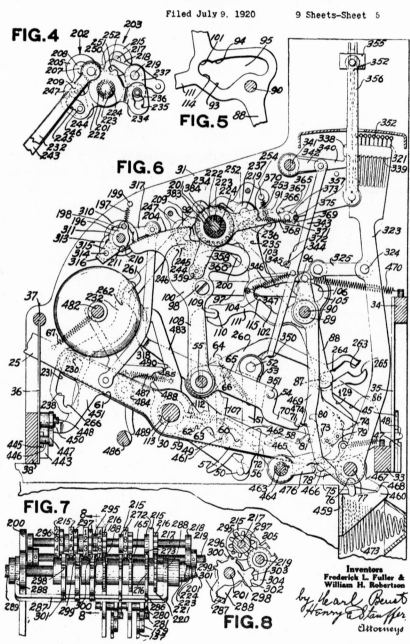

FIG.4

FIG.5

FIG.6

FIG.7

FIG.8

Inventors
Frederick L. Fuller &
William H. Robertson

by Hearl Benet
Henry E. Stauffer
Attorneys

A DIFFERENT manner of indicating figures on cash registers was provided by Mr. Fuller in a patent issued on March 1, 1927, and described as follows:

The main object of the invention is to provide such machines with new indicators, which are adapted to be differentially selected and then exposed to view.

Another object is to arrange the indicators in groups and to arrange the operating keys in groups, and to provide a mechanism whereby the operation of any key in any group directly selects a corresponding indicator in that respective group.

With these and incidental objects in view, the invention consists in certain novel features of construction and combination of parts, the essential elements of which are set forth in appended claims, and a preferred form of embodiment of which is hereinafter described with reference to the drawings which accompany and form part of the specification.

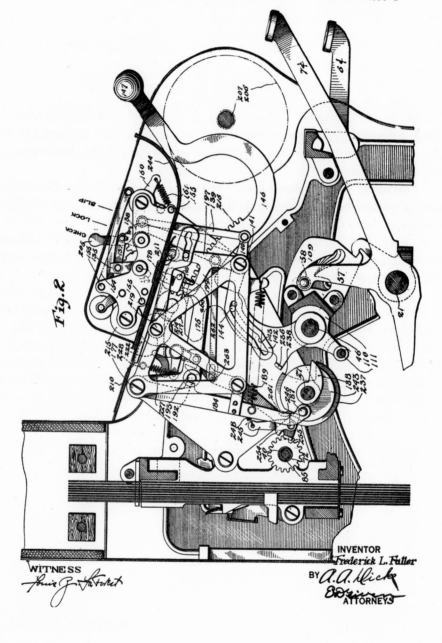

INVENTOR
Frederick L. Fuller
BY A.A. Hicks
ATTORNEYS

WITNESS

*A*NOTHER cash register, this time one that would correct sales errors, was born in the fertile Fuller brain prior to October 13, 1922, the date on which an application for patent was filed. Describing this improved cash register, the application stated:

Broadly, the object of the present invention is the provision of means whereby, if, through an anomalous operation of the machine, a record of the transaction is printed upon a check contained within the machine, this impression will be rendered illegible upon a subsequent operation of the machine and the record of the new transaction printed in the normal manner.

More specifically the object of the present invention is to provide a control lever for printing either upon an inserted slip or ejected strip, and if for any reason whatsoever, the machine be operated with the control lever in the slip printing position and without a slip inserted, the check paper will be positioned in such a manner that the impression made thereon will be obliterated during the next operation of the machine when the machine has been conditioned for printing on checks. The record of the transaction of the last operation will be printed in the usual manner, thus preventing confusion in the event that the records of more than one transaction appear upon an ejected check.

Jan. 15, 1929. **F. L. FULLER ET AL** 1,699,060

CASH REGISTER

Original Filed July 9, 1920 7 Sheets-Sheet 3

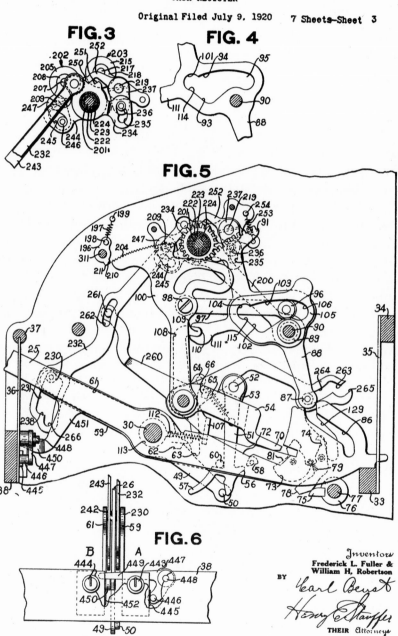

FIG. 3

FIG. 4

FIG. 5

FIG. 6

Inventors
Frederick L. Fuller &
William H. Robertson

BY Carl Beust
Henry C. Stauffer

THEIR Attorneys

*A*N IMPROVEMENT to the cash register patented on March 1, 1927, was developed by Mr. Fuller while the latter application was pending. The inventor said, in applying for patent on this improvement:

An object of this invention is to provide an improved totalizer actuating mechanism in machines known as the key-operated type.

Another object is to make such actuating mechanism function in connection with a plurality of totalizers.

Another object is to provide an improved totalizer selecting mechanism whereby the desired totalizer may be actuated by the common actuating mechanism.

Another object is to provide an improved totalizer engaging and disengaging mechanism for machines of the key-operated type.

Jan. 29, 1929.

F. L. FULLER

1,700,355

CALCULATING MECHANISM

Filed Feb. 14, 1918

8 Sheets—Sheet 2

FIG.2

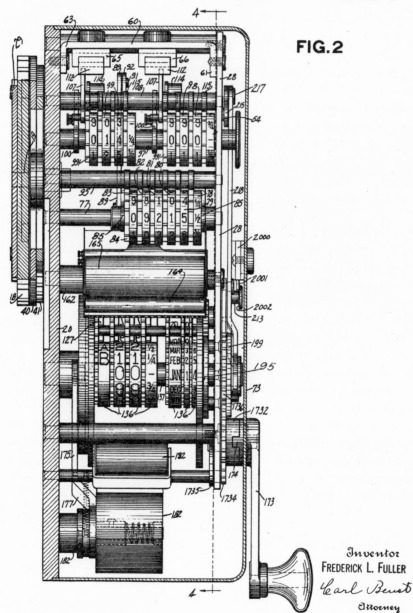

Inventor
FREDERICK L. FULLER

Carl Benst

Attorney

A CALCULATING mechanism for gasoline pumps, and other vending machines dispensing fluids, was covered in a patent granted Mr. Fuller in January 29, 1929, after the filing eleven years previously (Feb. 14, 1918), of an application which said:

This invention relates to improvements in calculating mechanisms, one object of which is to devise such an apparatus especially adapted for use with fluid dispensing pumps of the well known type used in the vending of gasoline or other fluids, the driving elements of the said calculating mechanism receiving actuation from driving pinions, which comprise the usual operating means for such pumps.

Another object of the present improvement is to provide such a calculating mechanism with means for measuring, registering, and recording in print the amount of fluid dispensed and also means for printing checks commensurate with the amount measured and registered, which checks are given to purchasers as receipts or statements.

Another object of the invention is to provide the calculating mechanism with a plurality of counters which will accumulate separately the amount of fluid sold by the different clerks.

A still further object of the present improvement is to provide a locking means for the pump and also for the calculating mechanism which can only be released by the insertion of keys held by the various clerks. Means is also provided whereby the impression producing mechanism is retained locked until the actuation of the pump, to deliver a predetermined quantity of fluid, is completed. This lock is for the purpose of insuring that a full measure of fluid be dispensed before a receipt therefor can be given the purchaser.

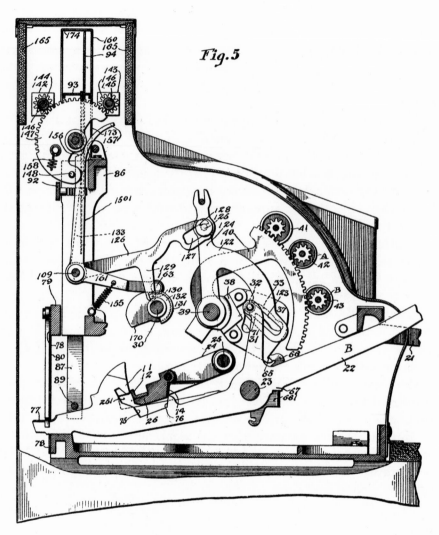

Fig.5

Fig.6

WITNESS

INVENTOR

Frederick L. Fuller

BY

ATTORNEYS

*I*MPROVEMENTS which had long been in Mr. Fuller's mind during all his work on cash registers, were assembled into one machine which was patented on June 4, 1929, and briefly described in the application as follows:

This invention relates to improvements in indicating mechanism for cash registers and accounting machines.

One object of the present invention is to provide an improved form of selecting mechanism for positively selecting indicators of the tablet type and retaining the selected indicators in their exposed position.

Another object is to provide an improved form of mechanism for adjusting rotatable indicators.

Another object is to arrange the groups of indicators within the machine and operate them in such a manner that the amount of the transaction will be rendered visible in its correct denominational order from both sides of the machine.

Another object of the present invention is to provide a new form of interlock between keys of different groups so as to compel an operation of a classification key before the operation of keys related to the transaction and denominational order groups.

More specifically it is an object of the present invention to devise an improved form of mechanism for elevating a vertically movable indicator carriage, in which are slidably mounted indicators of the tablet type, during the first operation of the machine; and means connected with the differential mechanism for selecting indicators identifying the keys depressed and retaining them in their elevated or exposed position during the second operation of the machine.

Aug. 27, 1929. F. L. FULLER 1,725,859

CASH REGISTER

Original Filed May 23, 1919 7 Sheets-Sheet 2

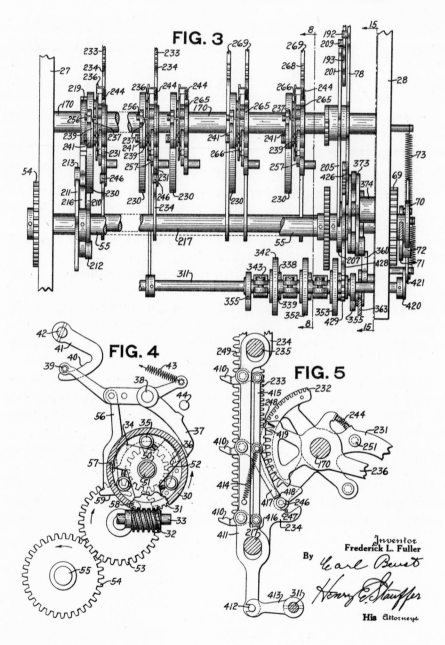

FIG. 3

FIG. 4

FIG. 5

Inventor
Frederick L. Fuller

By Earl Beust
Henry E. Stauffer

His Attorneys

STILL another improvement in cash registers was incorporated in a patent issued to Mr. Fuller on August 27, 1929, this one having the advantage of widening the mechanical registering abilities of the machine. In his application Mr. Fuller set forth that:

The invention relates to improvements in cash registers and the like, the primary object of which is to devise a machine having a registering mechanism capable of performing a large variety of functions, thus rendering it adaptable for use in many different businesses, and at the same time to so construct the machine that it is relatively simple and durable.

The objects of the present improvements are to provide:

An improved form of oscillating differential mechanism for controlling reciprocating actuators for positioning the various totalizers commensurate with the keys depressed.

An improved form of accumulating mechanism including a plurality of individual totalizers arranged in groups, such totalizers being carried by a frame which is easily removable from the machine and its connection with the operating elements for the totalizers, thus rendering them accessible for repair and providing a simple and cheap assembly.

An improved mechanism for selecting various individual totalizers for actuation by the differential actuators and a novel mechanism cooperating with the selecting mechanism for controlling the engagement of the various totalizers with the actuators as determined by the manipulative devices.

A novel aligning mechanism for the differential actuators and individual totalizers and the totalizer lines.

For combining the total lever control for the machine with the totalizer selecting and engaging mechanism whereby such mechanisms are controlled jointly by the total lever and by the manipulative devices.

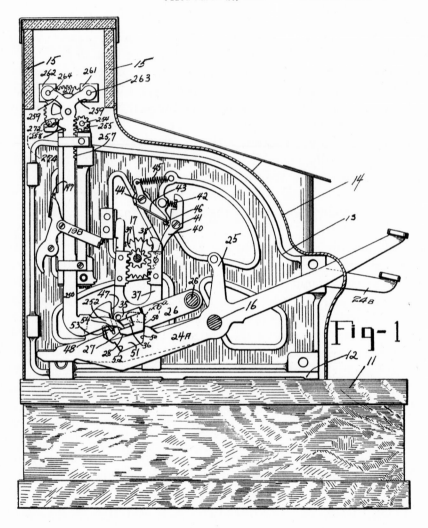

Fig-1

INVENTOR
FREDERICK L. FULLER

A. A. Hicke
ATTORNEY

WITNESS
Louis G. La Forest

I NCREASED speed in operation, combined with greater flexibility and simplicity, were embodied in a cash register patented by Mr. Fuller in September, 1929. This machine represented years of experiment, research and practice and Mr. Fuller applied for a patent believing that he had created the best cash register ever known. His description of the register said in part:

An object of my invention is the provision of a rotatable indicator which is differentially operable to one of a certain number of positions by the operation of one or more of a smaller number of keys.

A more specific object is the provision of a rotatable indicator movable to one of four positions by the actuation of one or two of three keys.

A further object relates to the provision of an improved flexible key arrangement. The term "flexible key arrangement" as understood in this art at the present time refers to a construction where a plurality of keys, which are each to be operated at a specified operation, may be successively given a partial preliminary movement, the final movement of the keys being effected by the further operation of one of the keys, so that by this means several keys which it is desired to operate at one time may be successively given a partial preliminary movement, the final movement of the keys being effected by the further operation of one of the keys, so that by this means several keys which it is desired to operate at one time may be successively started preliminarily and then all of the mechanism actuated thereby will be actuated by the depression of a single key, thus avoiding the spanning of several keys with one hand in order to secure the simultaneous operation of these several keys.

A further object is the provision of a flexible key arrangement so constructed that it may be utilized or not as preferred by the operator.

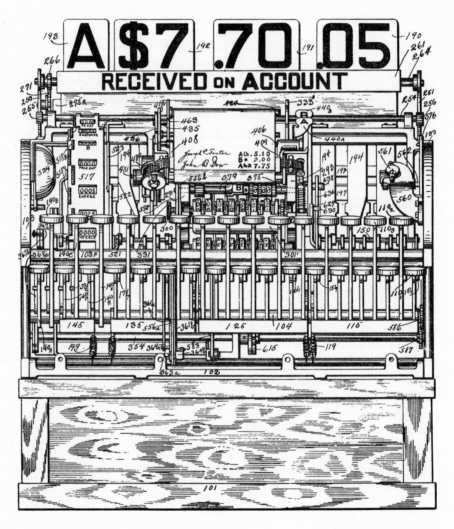

Fig-1

WITNESS

Louis F. La Forest

BY

INVENTOR

FREDERICK L. FULLER

A. A. Dicke

ATTORNEY

*C*LOSER check on those having access to cash registers was provided by a key operated register patented by Mr. Fuller on January 7, 1930. The purpose of this invention was described in the application as follows:

This invention relates to an improved key operated cash register, and has for its objects the provision of a generally improved machine of this type. Certain of the mechanisms disclosed herein are, nevertheless, adaptable to machines of other types than the key operated machine in connection with which they are shown.

More specific objects are the provision of an improved key action; improved tablet amount indicators; vertically reciprocatable rotatable transaction indicators, serving also as a flash; improved interlock, necessitating the operation of a clerk's key before other keys may be operated; flexible key coupler; improved counters and means for throwing them into and out of mesh with the differentially actuated registering segments at specified times; a segment frame lock; improved drawer release means; and, an improved arrangement of the special counters.

Another specially important object is the provision of an autographic record strip on which the details of each transaction are automatically recorded, and means for printing the totals accumulated on the counters on the strip.

Another object is the provision of an improved locking construction which permits the control of the machine by a single lock. A second lock may, however, be provided for giving access to the record strip so that it may be replaced by a clerk who would, nevertheless, not have access to the other parts of the machine.

Fig.6

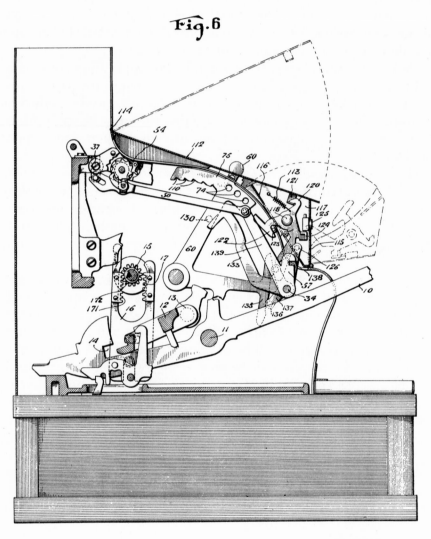

*B*ETTER locking and control in cash register operation was Mr. Fuller's next goal, and this was reached in a machine on which a patent was issued on April 8, 1930. Applying for this patent Mr. Fuller supplied the following general description of the machine:

While the improvements set forth in this application are shown applied to a particular type of cash register illustrated in the parent application, their utility is by no means limited to this specific embodiment. The improvements are of such a nature that they may be applied in various modifications to many other kinds of cash registers and accounting machines.

It is among the object of the present improvements to combine the various locking features which heretofore have been accomplished by separate devices under control of a number of locks in one common device, thus dispensing with the necessity of a number of controls and locks, together with multiplcation of numerous small parts of the machine.

It is customary in cash registers of the class embraced by the present invention to have a cash drawer released during each operation of the machine, together with a device to compel the closing of the drawer before the machine can be again operated. This aids in enforcing the proper records because it will be obvious that if the cash drawer must be closed before the register can be used again, records of the transactions must be entered in the machine as they occur, and the proprietor's protection is more nearly complete. Under certain circumstances, it is occasionally desirable to operate the register irrespective of the position of the cash drawer and for this reason the invention provides a device under the control of a lever which, by its proper adjustment, permits the machine to be operated in another way. The control lever is locked by means of a lock and key, and by keeping the lock key in his possession the proprietor has full control at all times over this locking mechanism.

April 8, 1930. F. L. FULLER 1,753,289

CASH REGISTER

Original Filed Nov. 19, 1918 3 Sheets-Sheet 2

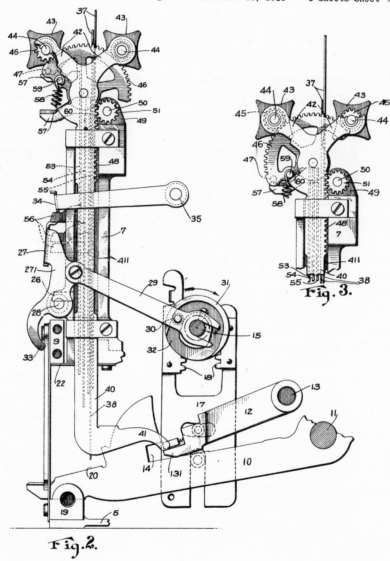

Fig. 2.

Fig. 3.

INVENTOR
Frederick L. Fuller
BY A. A. Hicks
ATTORNEY

*A*N IMPROVEMENT in the indicating mechanism of cash registers was patented April 8, 1920, by Mr. Fuller. The application for this patent stated:

The present invention contemplates combining the feature of a shield or "flash" with transaction indicators, the indicators being so arranged that the indication is spelled out in full, and not abbreviated. The transaction indicators in the present instance combine a plurality of bars for front and back indication and have character bearing faces, one for each of the following transaction keys "Paid out",—"Received on account",—and "Charge". The normal indication is "Cash" and is shown whenever an amount key is operated without a transaction key. The transaction bars are elevated at the same time as the tablet indicators, and prevent the raised indicators from being visible. As the raised indicators are held elevated the transaction bars are lowered. If no transaction keys have been depressed the bars will not be adjusted but will indicate "Cash." If, however, a transaction key has been depressed the bars will be adjusted during their return and exhibit the desired indication.

The invention further provides a color scheme for the tranaction indicators. Each transaction key has usually associated therewith a particular color of a "color system." The bars in the present instance are also colored so that even though the legend upon the transaction bar would not be visible at a distance it would still be possible to discern the color on the face exhibited and from this deduce the type of transaction which has been entered in the machine.

April 29, 1930. F. L. FULLER **1,756,350**

CASH REGISTER

Original Filed May 23, 1919 2 Sheets-Sheet 2

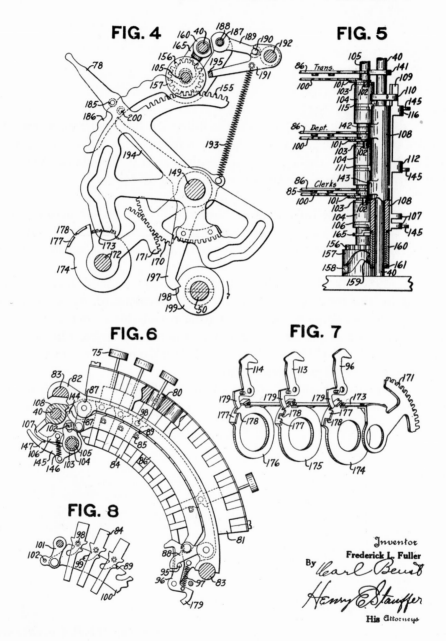

FIG. 4

FIG. 5

FIG. 6

FIG. 7

FIG. 8

Inventor
Frederick L. Fuller
By Carl Beust
Henry E. Stauffer
His Attorneys

*E*LEVEN years elapsed between the filing of the application and the actual granting of a patent on another improvement for cash registers. Filed in May, 1919, the application resulted in a patent dated April 29, 1930. Its provisions were briefly summarized as follows:

The objects of the present improvement are to provide:

A novel release mechanism, controlled by various manipulative devices, so constructed that a certain predetermined number of manipulative devices must be operated before the release of the machine is effected.

To combine with the release mechanism, above mentioned, a device actuated by the total lever so that, after movement of the total lever, to control the machine to perform a total or sub-total operation, a manipulative device in any bank selected by the total lever may be operated to effect the release of the machine, the manipulative devices in the other banks being locked against operation.

An improved form of interlocking mechanism controlled by the total lever and co-operating with the zero stop pawls of the various control banks of manipulative devices.

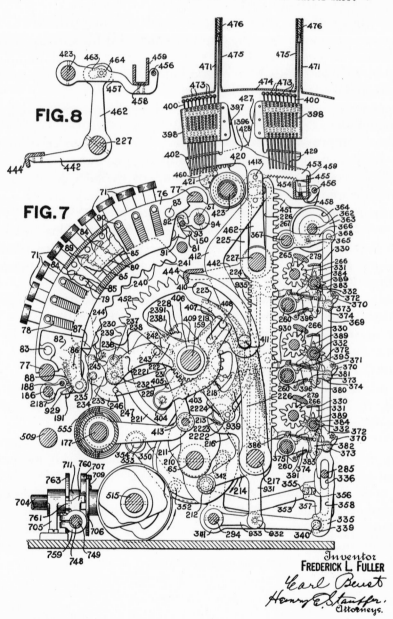

FIG.8

FIG.7

Inventor
FREDERICK L. FULLER
Earl Beust
Henry C. Stauffer.
Attorneys.

*A*NOTHER set of improvements patented by Mr. Fuller for use on cash registers set forth that:

The objects of the present improvement are to provide:

A novel machine release mechanism controlled by various manipulative devices, so constructed that a certain predetermined number of manipulative devices must be actuated before the release of the machine is effected, and a novel form of key bank.

To combine with the release mechanism heretofore mentioned, total and sub-total devices actuated by a lever.

Also an improved form of oscillating differential mechanism controlling reciprocating actuators for positioning the indicators and various totalizers commensurate with the values of the keys depressed.

An improved form of accumulating mechanism comprising a plurality of individual totalizers arranged in group.

A novel form of transfer mechanism for the individual totalizers.

An improved mechanism for selecting various individual totalizers and a novel mechanism cooperating with the selecting mechanism for controlling the engagement of the various totalizers.

A novel aligning mechanism for the differential actuators, indicator mechanism, individual totalizers, and the totalizer lines.

An improved form of interlocking mechanism controlled by the total lever and cooperating with the zero stop pawls of the various control banks of manipulative devices.

A printing mechanism having various novel features and so constructed, that a record strip, check and inserted slip may be printed during one operation of the machine.

A severing device and a perforating device cooperating with the printing mechanism whereby a check issued by the printing mechanism is severed from the strip.

A novel mechanism for setting the various type wheels commensurate with the values of the keys depressed, and an impression device constructed so that the platens for taking impressions on the various printing mediums are held stationary and the type wheels themselves are moved thereagainst to make impressions.

June 3, 1930. F. L. FULLER 1,761,719

CASH REGISTER

Original Filed May 23, 1919 2 Sheets-Sheet 2

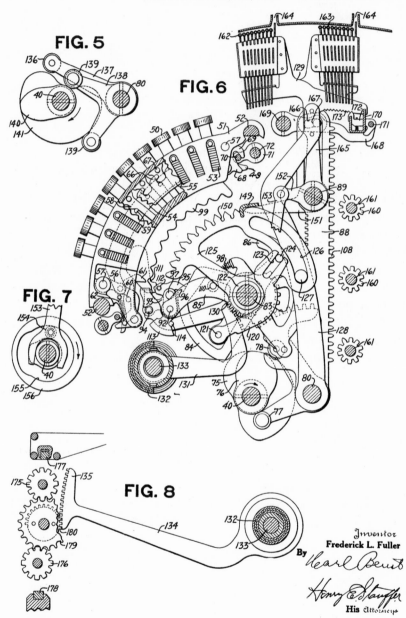

FIG. 5

FIG. 6

FIG. 7

FIG. 8

Inventor
Frederick L. Fuller
By Carl Beust
Henry E. Stauffer
His Attorneys

STUDY and research were practically continuous with Mr. Fuller at this step of his career, and one of the patents granted him was described in the following words:

The objects of the present improvement are to provide:

An improved form of oscillating differential mechanism adapted to control reciprocating actuators for positioning totalizers, and to control the setting or positioning of indicators and printers.

A novel form of connection intermediate the differential actuator and the indicators and printers.

A novel aligning mechanism for the differential and the indicators.

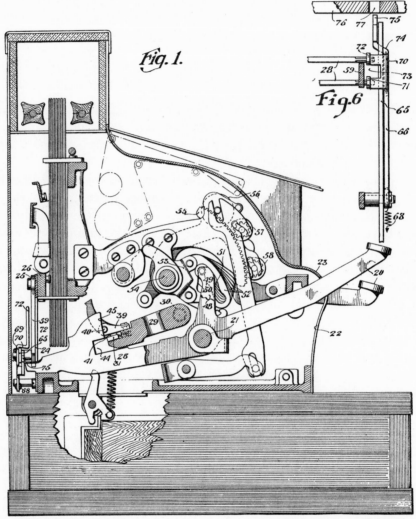

Fig.1.

Fig.6

Inventor

Frederick. L. Fuller.

By *A. A. Wicke*

Attorney

CORRECTION of a tendency in certain cash registers to enter incorrect transactions was accomplished by an improvement on which Mr. Fuller was granted a patent on June 17, 1930. The application on which this patent was granted said:

A practical objection which has been found in the use of that type of machine whereby the keys may be successively attached to the key coupler is that keys of certain groups may inadvertently be slightly depressed beyond a certain point and since the mistake cannot be corrected the amount represented by that key would have to be indicated and registered whether it corresponds to the amount of the sale or not. It is an object of the present invention to provide improved means associated with certain keys and in connection with the interlocking devices, whereby the key coupler may not be moved beyond a position in which keys may be connected therewith, even though the keys are operated violently and with considerable force. This mechanism is positive in its action, precluding any possibility of the disarrangement of the machine performed either accidentally, or intentionally by prejudiced persons.

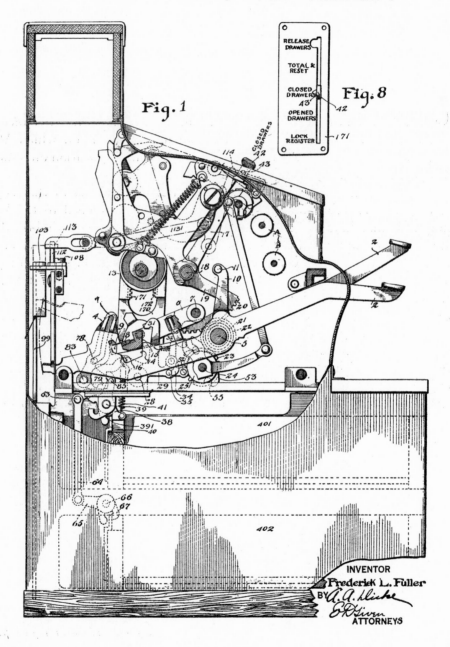

Fig. 1

Fig. 8

RELEASE DRAWERS

TOTAL & RESET

CLOSED DRAWERS 43

OPENED DRAWERS

LOCK REGISTER

INVENTOR
Frederick L. Fuller
BY
ATTORNEYS

*I*MPROVEMENT was the keynote of most of Mr. Fuller's cash register inventions, and this was reflected in the vastly better cash registers that were presented to customers from year to year. One improvement, patented April 7, 1937, was described as follows:

One object of the invention is to provide an improved construction for selectively operating a plurality of independent cash drawers.

Another object is to provide an improved mechanism for selectivity ringing bells or sounding equivalent alarms to call attention to the opening of the different drawers, in connection with mechanism for preventing such alarms when desired.

In the accompanying drawings the improvements are shown in one form which they might take when applied to or embodied in a machine of the type shown and described in U. S. application Serial No. 263,125 filed Nov. 19, 1918, by Frederick L. Fuller, as well as British Patents 135,465; 157,823; 157,824; and 157,825 granted for the same invention. This embodiment is only illustrative, however, as the improvements are capable of modification and change to permit applying them to machines of various types and it is the desire not to be limited to the form herein shown and described.

FIG.2.

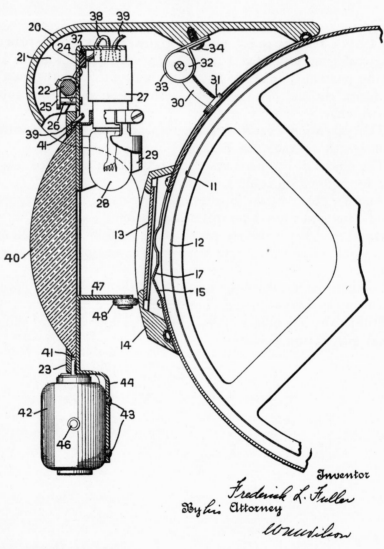

Inventor

Frederick L. Fuller

By his Attorney

WM Wilson

*M*ANY years after Mr. Fuller's original activity in the field of computing scales, he perfected a magnifying device that was far ahead of anything previously made to enable the customer and the merchant to read the weight and price on a sale with greater ease. The application set forth that:

This invention relates to scales, especially of the computing type provided with a rotable drum chart.

The object of the invention is to provide an improved magnifying device for facilitating reading of the chart.

Another object of the invention is to provide an illuminating device for said chart and a novel control means therefor.

Another object is also the provision of a switch for said illuminating device which is adapted to serve as a handle to manipulate the magnifying device.

Further, the object of the invention is the provision of novel means for carrying lead wires to said illuminating device.

Still further, an object is the provision of a novel guard and support for said magnifying device.

Dec. 29, 1931. F. L. FULLER 1,839,174

CASH REGISTER

Original Filed Oct. 9, 1922. 3 Sheets-Sheet 1

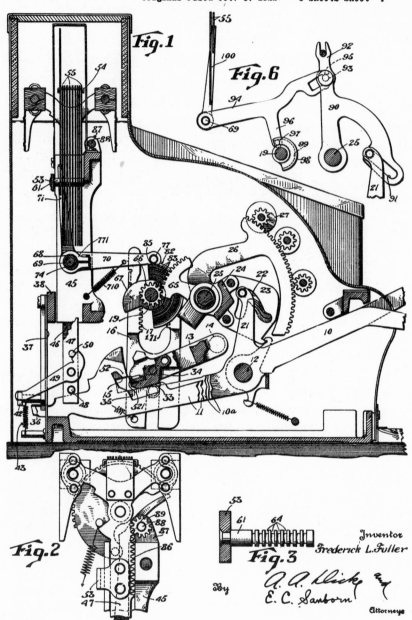

Fig. 1

Fig. 6

Fig. 2

Fig. 3

Inventor
Frederick L. Fuller

By A. A. Hicks and E. C. Sanborn

Attorneys

*C*ASH registers being operated by clerks of widely varying degrees of intelligence, the improvements patented from time to time had as their aim the presentation of practically foolproof mechanisms. Such an improvement was patented on December 29, 1931, by Mr. Fuller. The application stated:

This invention relates more particularly to cash registers of that class in which the keys are divided into different groups, such as, amount keys and classification keys, so that a depression of keys in different groups may result not only in an indication of amounts but also of special characters to designate the classification of the sale registered, so that in this way each sale may be completely identified. To insure the proper indication, it is desirable to provide an interlocking mechanism between the different groups of keys so that it is always necessary to depress one of the classification keys with an amount key.

It is the main object of the present invention to provide an improved form of inter-locking mechanism for effectively performing this function and which is simple in construction, but positive in its action thus precluding any possibilitiy of the disarrangement of the machine, either accidentally or intentionally.

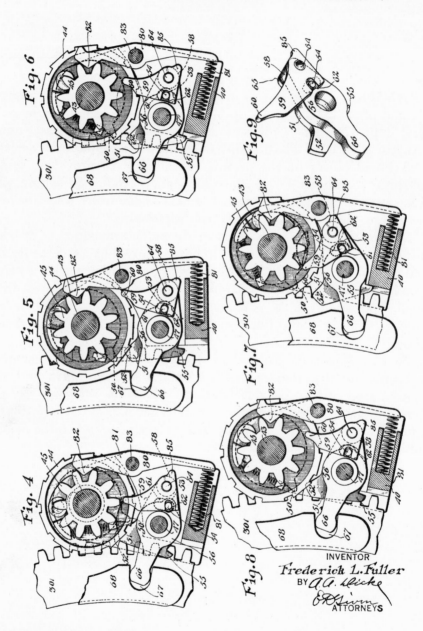

INVENTOR

Frederick L. Fuller

BY A. A. Wicke

ATTORNEYS

*T*RANSFER mechanisms in cash registers were subject to improvement and presented a fascinating field for inventive genius. One of the several improvements of this sort designed by Mr. Fuller was patented on August 23, 1932. The description in the patent application declared:

A broad object of the present invention is to provide a suitable mechanism for positively transmitting motion from each adding wheel of a lower order to the adding wheel of next higher order when the lower order adding wheel has completed a full rotation.

More specifically it is an object of the present invention to provide a transfer mechanism comprising a trip pawl actuated by a trip device associated with the wheel of the lower order to set a transfer pawl in its transfer position, so that when a separately operated arm is oscillated during a regular operation of the machine the transfer pawl describes a path which intercepts a tooth of the next higher order totalizer wheel thereby effecting a transfer.

Further objects of the present invention are to prevent accidental displacement of the totalizer wheels when out of engagement with their actuating segments, to provide frictional means for retaining the components of the transfer mechanism in their set position and to preclude the possibility of over-carrying of the totalizer wheel when the machine is subjected to improper usage.

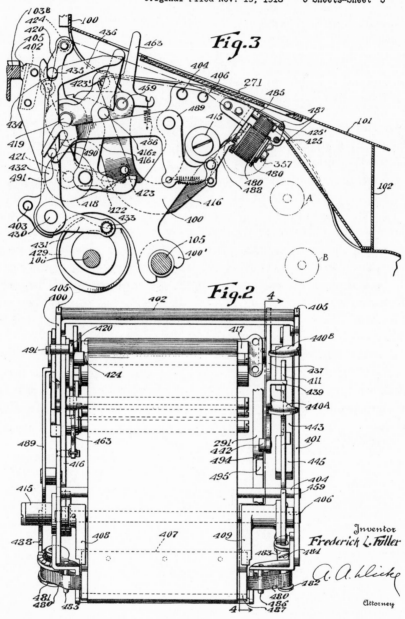

Fig.3

Fig.2

Inventor
Frederick L. Fuller

A. A. Wicke
Attorney

*T*HE cash register patented by Mr. Fuller on January 7, 1930, was improved by a patent issued in August, 1932, on an application which contained the following description:

A cash register of the type described in the parent application, above identified, comprises sets of keys representing numbers and other data, and registering and indicating devices under the control of said keys. A single registering device or totalizer may be provided for accumulating a total of all the items entered in the machine, or a plurality of totalizers may be provided for segregating the items entered in the register according to any desired classification. Such machines may also be provided with mechanism for printing records of the various transactions entered therein, and, likewise, printing the segregated totals accumulated by the plurality of registering devices.

It is the purpose of the present invention to improve the construction of the printing mechanism generally, and to this end the invention comprises improvements in such parts of the printer as impression taking, impression point shifting, ribbon feeding, and record strip feeding and shifting.

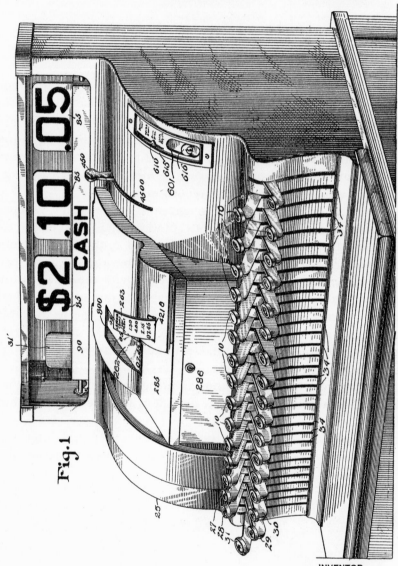

Fig.1

INVENTOR

Fredcrick L. Fuller

BY *A. A. Blecke*

H. C. Diesened

ATTORNEYS

*M*ORE expensive record keeping was the object of an improvement to cash registers patented by Mr. Fuller on August 30, 1932. His application for a patent stated:

One object of the present invention is the provision of a plurality of accumulating devices for accumulating the amounts of the items entered into the machine and suitable printing mechanism for printing the totals standing thereon upon suitable record material.

A further object of the present invention is the provision of separate operating means for recording the totals standing upon each of the totalizers in conjunction with suitable mechanism for restoring the accumulating elements to zero after the total has been recorded. More specifically it is an object of the present invention to provide means for printing the items entered in the machine upon suitable record material which is issued from the machine and a suitable manipulative means operable at will for recording the total of the items accumulated upon the record material and restoring the accumulator to zero as an incident to accumulating a subsequent set of items. A further object is the provision of a second accumulator for accumulating the grand total of all the individual items entered in the machine as well as suitable recording mechanism for printing the grand totals.

Another object is to provide suitable controlling and interlocking devices to insure operation of various features in correct relation to the operation of other features.

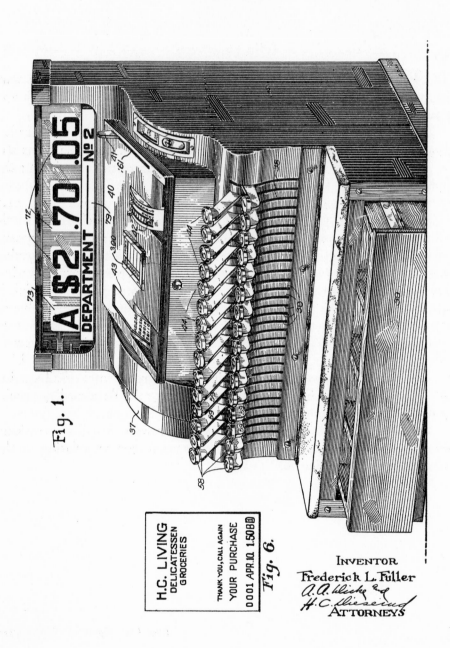

Fig. 1.

Fig. 6.

H.C. LIVING
DELICATESSEN
GROCERIES

THANK YOU, CALL AGAIN
YOUR PURCHASE
0001 APR.10 1.50B

INVENTOR
Frederick L. Fuller

ATTORNEYS

*C*LOSER analysis of the transactions recorded on a typewriter was the object of patent No. 1,874,276. Mr. Fuller applied for this patent with the following introductory description:

One object of the present invention is to adapt the register for a segregate analysis of transactions by the provision of a plurality of totalizers with mechanism capable of a preliminary adjustment to establish cooperative realtion between anyone of the said totalizers and a common totalizer operating means.

A further object of the present invention is to provide improved mechanism for printing the amounts of each transaction and certain identifying characters upon a record strip which is contained within the machine. An improved mechanism is also provided for the present machine capable of printing, in addition to the amounts, dates, identifying characters and certain other matter upon checks which are issued from the machine. Associated with the check printing mechanism is a novel driving mechanism for the electro as well as certain other accessory mechanisms.

A still further object of the present invention is to provide a simple and effective mechanism for locking the keys in their depressed positions and means for freeing them after an operation of the check issuing lever.

Still another object of the present invention is to provide means for preventing a second depression of the keys until the check issuing lever is returned to its normal position.

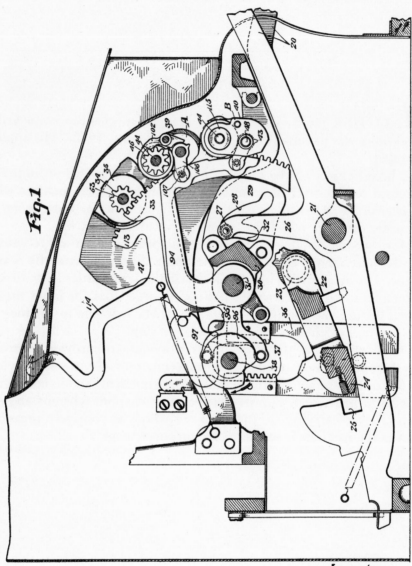

Fig.1

Inventor
Friderick L. Fuller
By
a. a. Wicke
Attorney

$\mathcal{A}$NOTHER improvement to the transfer mechanism employed in cash registers was patented by Mr. Fuller in August, 1932. His application stated:

A broad object of the present invention is to provide an improved mechanism for positively transmitting motion from each totalizer wheel of a lower order to the totalized wheel of the next higher order when the lower order totalizer wheel has completed a full rotation.

More specifically it is an object of the present invention to provide a transfer mechanism comprising a tripping device actuated by a tripping member associated with the wheel of the lower order so as to set a transfer trip tooth in its transfer position in order that the latter may be actuated during the continued operation of the machine to advance the totalizer wheel of the next higher order one step.

Other objects of the present invention are to provide improved means for preventing accidental displacement of the totalizer wheels when out of engagement with their actuating segments and in connection therewith to provide an improved type of mechanism whereby the possibility of over-carrying of the totalizer wheels is positively prevented whenever the machine is subjected to improper usage.

Sept. 20, 1932.   F. L. FULLER   1,878,125

ACCOUNTING MACHINE

Filed Nov. 19, 1927   8 Sheets—Sheet 1

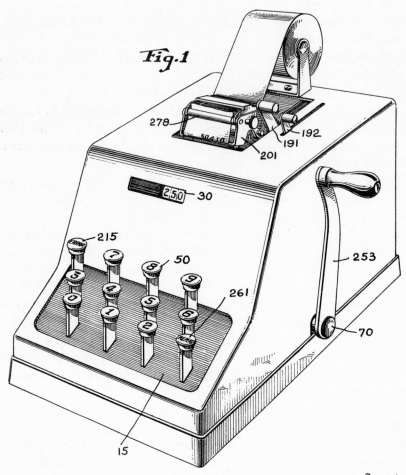

Fig.1

Inventor

Frederick L Fuller

By Cooper, Kerr & Dunham

his Attorneys

*T*HE first of Mr. Fuller's accounting machine inventions for the International Business Machines Corporation was patented on September 20, 1932. Of this invention he said, in his patent application:

This invention relates generally to adding and listing machines, and has particular reference to improvements in adding and listing machines of the kind which list items, accumulate items into a total, and print the totals whenever desired.

The various ideas involved in this invention are shown in the accompanying drawings in the form they would take when embodied in a ten-key adding machine, but, as will be clear later on, some of the features can be used just as well in adding machines in which the various functions are controlled in ways other than by a ten-key keyboard.

One of the objects of the invention is to provide a simple, sturdy machine which will list items, accumulate the items into totals, and give printed totals or sub-totals, whenever desired.

Another object of the invention is to provide a machine having all of the characteristics just stated which will perform all of its functions acccurately over a long period of time with a minimum amount of adjustment or repair.

Still another object is to provide a printing mechanism for listing and printing totals and sub-totals which is extremely simple and efficient, and in which the ribbon or corresponding carrier for marking material may be replaced or supplied without the trouble and inconvenience necessary to re-ink or change ink ribbons and the like used at the present time in machines now in general use.

Another object of the invention is to provide a machine which will perform all of the more important functions of an adding and listing machine, but which can nevertheless be manufactured at a very low cost, with a corresponding low selling price to the purchasing public.

Oct. 25, 1932. F. L. FULLER 1,883,894

CASH REGISTER

Filed Dec. 3, 1926 3 Sheets-Sheet 1

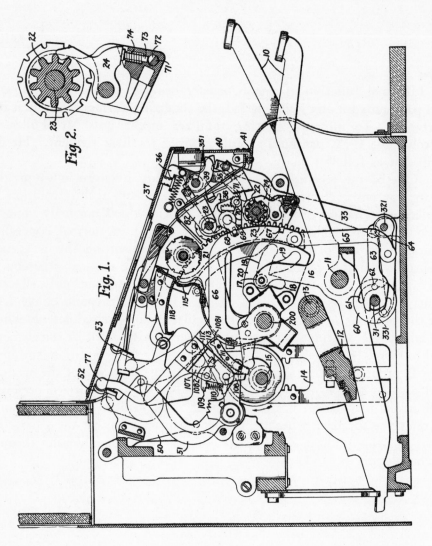

Fig. 2.

Fig. 1.

INVENTOR
FREDERICK L. FULLER
BY A. A. Wicke and
H. C. Wiesend
ATTORNEYS

*T*HE final function of a cash register being to record the total sales and payments for any given period, the totalizing devices are of first importance. To improve existing totalizer mechanisms Mr. Fuller on October 25, 1932, patented a tamper proof totalizer element. He described it as follows:

One of the specific objects of the present invention is to provide means for positively locking the totalizer elements against rotation by any means whatsoever when the lid or shield which normally conceals these elements is released for movement out of its normal concealing position. In the present embodiment of the invention this is accomplished by suitable connections from a controlling element whereby, as the latter releases the concealing lid or shield, it simultaneously effects a positive locking of the totalizer wheels. It has been found convenient, for this purpose, to make use of the regular spring-pressed detents which are effective at all times, to prevent accidental movement of the elements and to merely positively hold these detents under the conditions specified.

In order to further safeguard the resetting operations of the machine and prevent tampering with this mechanism by unauthorized persons a full stroke mechanism has been applied to a member which is adapted to reset the totalizer wheels. This mechanism prevents the partial resetting of the totalizer elements without carrying the operation through to completion.

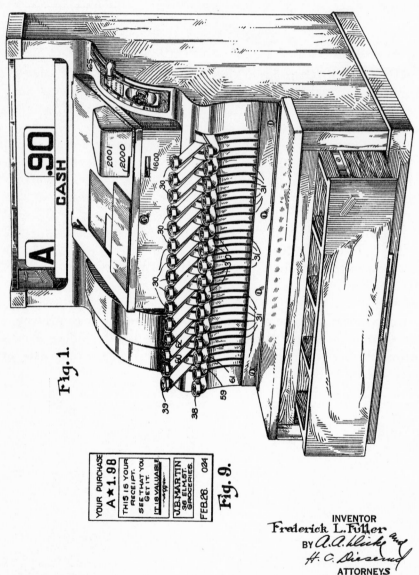

Feb. 21, 1933. F. L. FULLER 1,898,045

CASH REGISTER

Filed April 1, 1926 6 Sheets-Sheet 1

A
.90
CASH
2001
2000
1600
165
30
31
38
39
59
60
61
62

Fig. 1.

YOUR PURCHASE
A★1.98
THIS IS YOUR RECEIPT. SEE THAT YOU GET IT.
IT IS VALUABLE
J.B.MARTIN
38 ELM ST.
GROCERIES.
FEB.26. 024

Fig. 9.

INVENTOR
Frederick L. Fuller
BY A. A. Wicke and H. C. Diesend
ATTORNEYS

PRINTING mechanisms in cash registers increased their value to users and in order to provide better printing than was then being done Mr. Fuller patented on February 21, 1933, an improvement in printing devices which he described in the application as follows:

A broad object of the invention is to provide a printing mechanism for printing and issuing checks or printing upon sales slips inserted to receive impressions, preferably with an automatic device whereby the mechanism may be conditioned for either check printing or sales slip printing.

Another object of the invention is to provide interlocking devices effective to insure correct operation of the improved machine as a whole when the printing mechanism is in check printing condition; and automatic devices by means of which the interlocking devices may be rendered ineffective when the machine is to be utilized for printing upon an inserted sales slip. In the present preferred embodimnt th printing mchanism comprises devices for printing certain data including devices for printing the serial or consecutive numbers as well as the date of the transaction upon issued checks.

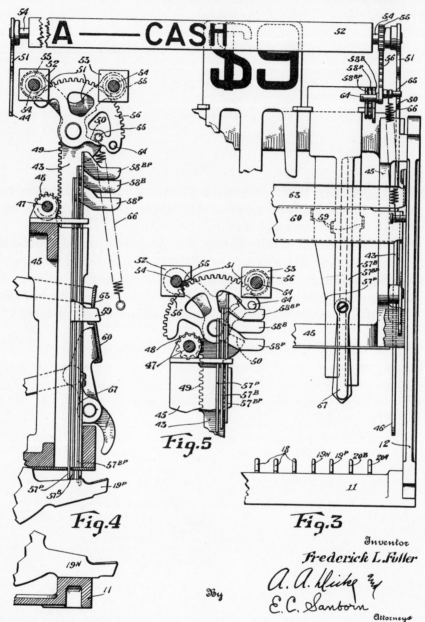

March 14, 1933.

F. L. FULLER

1,901,093

CASH REGISTER

Original Filed March 20, 1919

2 Sheets-Sheet 2

A——CASH
$9
Fig.4
Fig.5
Fig.3

Inventor

Frederick L. Fuller

By A. A. Wicke

E. C. Sanborn

Attorneys

ONCE MORE Mr. Fuller turned his attention to the improvement of cash register indicating mechanisms. The application which resulted in a patent for this improvement stated:

The main object of this invention is to provide a rotatable indicator which is differentially operable to one of a certain number of positions by the operation of one or more of a smaller number of keys.

A more specific object is the provision of a rotatable indicator movable to one of four positions by the actuation of one or two of three keys.

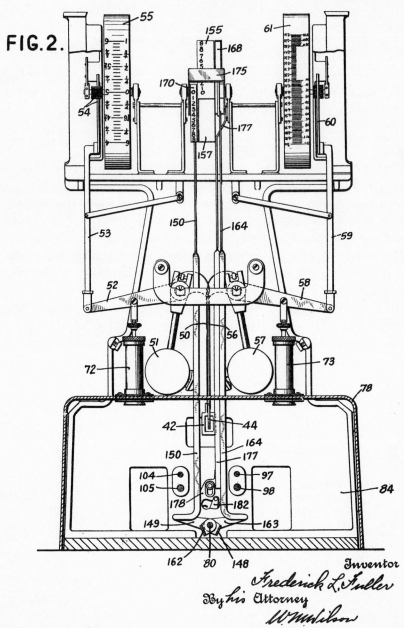

FIG.2.

Inventor

Frederick L. Fuller

By his Attorney

W. M. Wilson

*A*NOTHER computing scale was patented by Mr. Fuller on March 21, 1933, and in applying for this patent he said:

This case relates to weighing and computing scales and particularly to one in which a computing chart is variously operated in accordance with different, selected factors of the weight.

The object of this invention in general is to provide novel and improved mechanism for selecting the factors in accordance with which the computing chart is to be operated.

More specifically in connection with factor levers which associate the computing chart with the load support, it is an object to provide rotatably mounted, rockable, nested members for controlling the factor levers.

FIG.I.

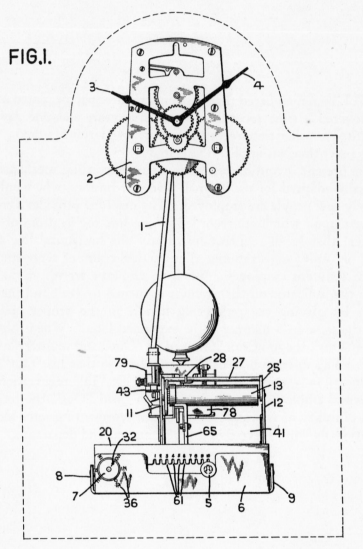

Inventor

F. L. Fuller

By his Attorney

W. N. Wilson

*I*T WILL be remembered that Mr. Fuller's first patent, dated March 20, 1888, covered a time recorder. Forty-five years and one day later he was granted another time recorder patent, on March 21, 1933. Describing this invention, his application stated:

The present invention relates to a time recording mechanism which is especially adapted for use in small places of business where only a comparatively few people are employed. The machine provides a continuous time sheet upon which are recorded in one line registrations of the same character; that is, all registrations in any one horizontal line are either all "In" or "Out" registrations. The vertical columns represent registrations for different employes. When an employe arrives at the place of business the indicator on the machine is turned to "In" and the employe registers by placing the registering handle in the proper position and lifting the same in a manner to be explained later. When this employe registers "Out" the indicator is moved to "Out" and registers in the same manner. This operation feeds the time sheet so that his "Out" registration appears in vertical alinement under his "In" registration so that after several employes have registered "In" and "Out" the record sheet shows a plurality of columns, each column representing some individual's registration showing successive times of arrival and departure.

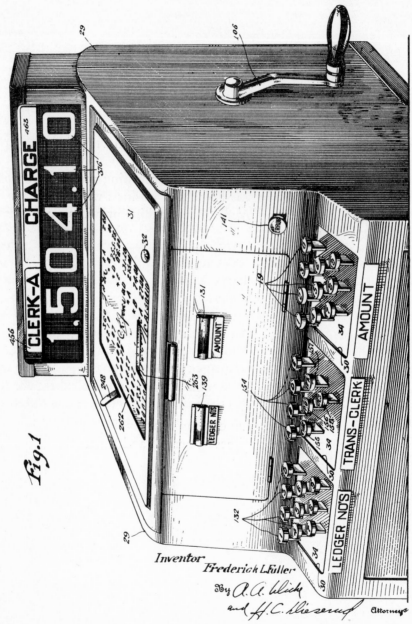

Fig.1

Inventor

Frederick L.Fuller

By a. a. black

and H. C. Chiesind   Attorneys

A CASH register capable of registering large amounts of cash and performing many other complicated tasks with comparative simplicity was patented by Mr. Fuller, whose application for patent stated:

In the form of the invention as herein disclosed a series of ten keys is adated to successively control the positioning of a series of type carriers and selector wheels which, after being positioned under control of a depressed key, are stepped laterally to carry one of the type carriers and one of the wheels into engagement with detaining devices, while the remaining carriers and wheels of the series are turned to zero positions. After a number of carriers and wheels have thus been set and shifted into engagement with the detaining devices other mechanism is brought into play to control the differential operation of a totalizer and positioning of indicators in accordance with the setting of the selector wheels.

In connection with the differential mechanism, an object is the provision of a novel form of escapement mechanism for positively moving the selectors, which are moved into positions controlled by the keys, into operative relationship with the racks which control the differential positioning of the accumulating and indicating mechanism.

FIG. 1

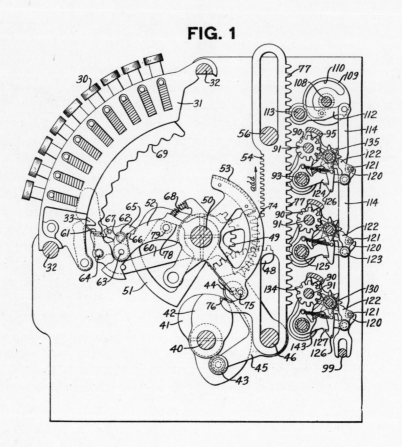

Inventor
Frederick L. Fuller
By *Earl Benst*
Henry E. Stauffer
His Attorney

*T*OTALIZERS, an all-important factor of cash register operation, were brought to greater perfection in a patent obtained by Mr. Fuller on October 10, 1933. The application stated:

One object of this invention is to provide a novel form of transfer mechanism for totalizers. The transfer mechanism may be used with a plurality of totalizers. In the present application a plurality of totalizers and transfer mechanisms are shown, and the transfer mechanisms are arranged so as to be operated by a common driving mechanism. The transfer mechanism shown herein, being operated by a single driving mechanism, has its advantages over other types of transfer mechanisms used in connection with a plurality of totalizers in that, in the present case, by the use of the single driving mechanism, the number of parts is materially reduced.

Another object of this invention is to arrange the actuators, totalizers and transfer mechanism in such a way as to permit the transfer mechanism to be operated wholly independently of the actuating mechanism. By the use of this construction more time may be given to the means for operating the transfer mechanism; hence, a more reliable transfer is obtained.

Feb. 13, 1934. F. L. FULLER 1,946,906

SORTING MACHINE OF THE MANUAL CONTROL TYPE

Original Filed Oct. 21, 1930 10 Sheets-Sheet 9

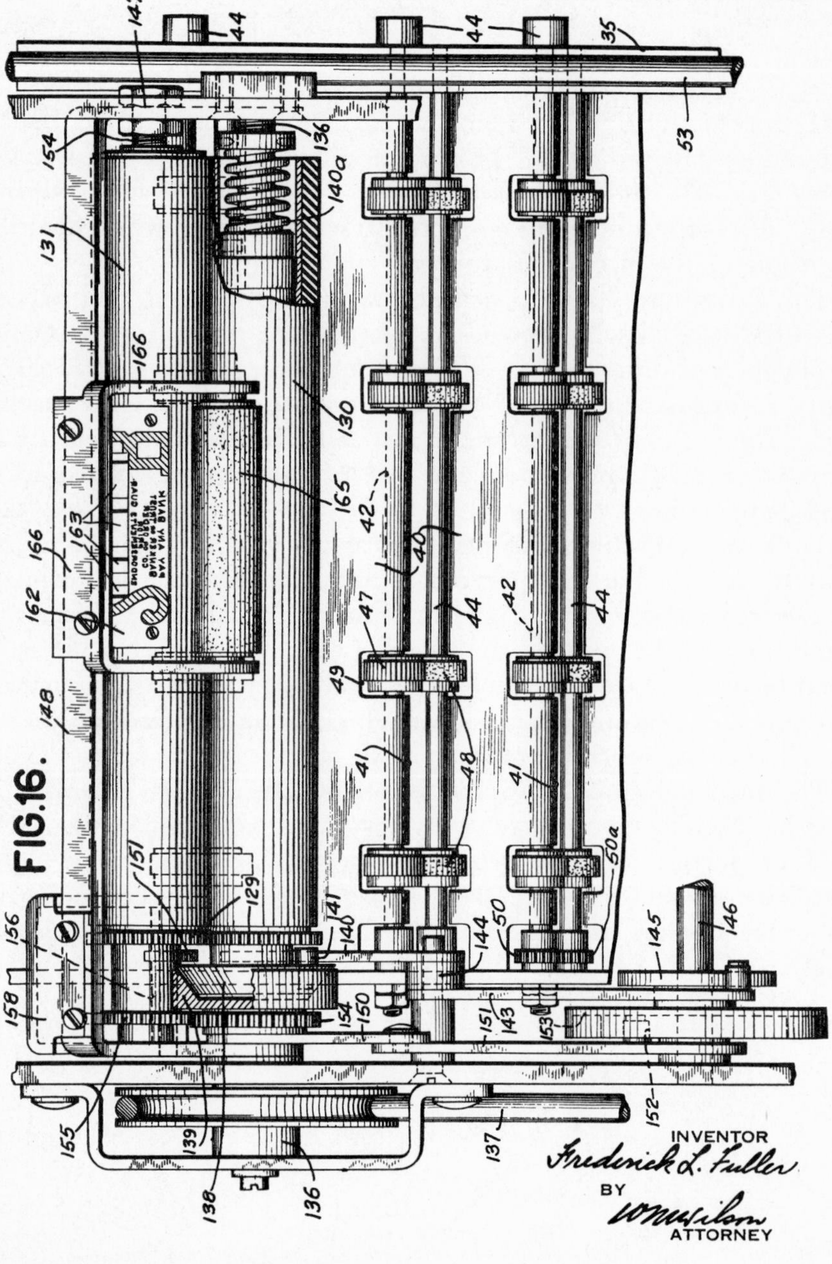

FIG.16.

INVENTOR
Frederick L. Fuller
BY
W.M. Wilson
ATTORNEY

*T*HE International Proof Machine for Banks was invented by Mr. Fuller and patented in 1934. The first application for a patent was filed October 21, 1930, and a division of this application was filed February 6, 1932. Patent was issued first on the latter application, which described the purpose of the machine as follows:

This invention relates to sorting machines in general, and particularly to the type in which provision is made for sorting under manual control papers of different classification such papers consisting of, checks, receipts, cards or the like. An extended feature of the present machine provides for not only sorting the papers but effecting some type of endorsement or designation upon one face of the paper delivered to the sorting compartment.

The present machine, however, is so arranged that it may be utilized separately as a sorting machine or an endorsing machine and while in the preferred employment of the machine the combined functions are preferably utilized to gain all the benefits, the invention is not limited to the combination as each of the features and many of the improvements residing in such features are applicable singly or in combination, to machines of the same or other types.

The machine embodying the various features thus generally described has been designed particularly for use in banks and by the inclusion of the sorting and endorsing functions is able to effect, to a great extent, a considerable saving in labor now required in the accounting and distribution systems of the check departments of banks and clearing houses.

FIG.1.

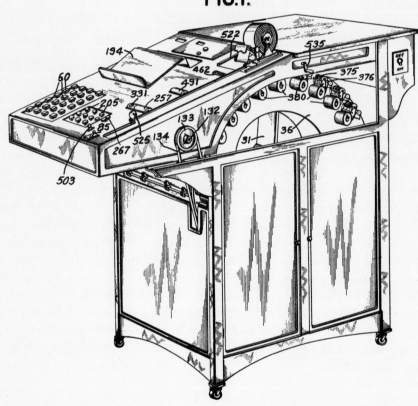

Inventor
F. L. Fuller
By his Attorney
W M Wilson

*T*HE original application for a patent on the International Proof Machine for banks resulted in the issuance of a patent on July 17, 1934. Describing the general method of handsorting checks received from depositors, and drawn on many different banks, the application said:

By the employment of the present machine a "block" of checks may be sorted into twenty-four different classifications. As a check is sorted the amount represented on the check is also printed upon a strip associated with the compartment selected. The total of such amounts may also be printed upon the strip to give a total of the checks of the same classification. When such listings are effected upon the individual classification strips, there is also listed upon a "control strip" the amount indicated on each check sorted and these listings are made in exactly the same sequential arrangement as on the deposit tickets. A total of the item listings given by the machine must agree with the total derived from the deposit tickets and if a discrepancy is observed a comparison between the listings on the deposit tickets and those on the control strip is required. An error will readily be noted by the preservation of the listings in the original sequence.

Feb. 5, 1935. F. L. FULLER 1,989,976

SORTING AND PRINTING MACHINE

Original Filed Oct. 21, 1930 17 Sheets-Sheet 1

FIG. 1.

FIG. 7.

FIG. 6.

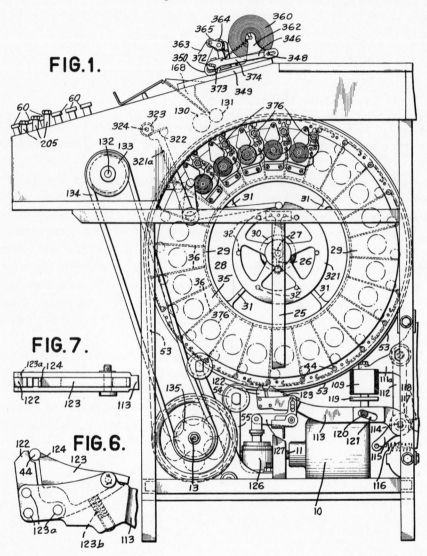

INVENTOR
Frederick L. Fuller
BY
W. M. Wilson
ATTORNEY

*A*NOTHER patent on improvements in the Proof Machine for banks was taken out by Mr. Fuller on February 5, 1935. The application stated:

Considering the portion of the machine employed for the purpose of printing the items represented on the checks sorted and other functions, it is the main object of the invention to provide means to effect the listings of the items represented upon checks entered in a compartment upon a related record strip. To carry out this object the drum having the check receiving compartments is provided with a series of record strip printing mechanism, there being a record strip for each compartment. When a compartment is brought to position for receiving a check by depression of the related key there will be brought to printing position a related record strip.

It is a still further object of the invention to provide in the machine item indicating wheels controlled by 10 keys which inform the operator the item to be later set up in the item printing devices. Since the items are set up on indicating wheels prior to the setting up of the item printing devices the operator is able to check for errors the items to be printed.

Feb. 19, 1935. F. L. FULLER 1,991,551

CASH REGISTER

Original Filed April 1, 1926 5 Sheets-Sheet 1

FIG. 1

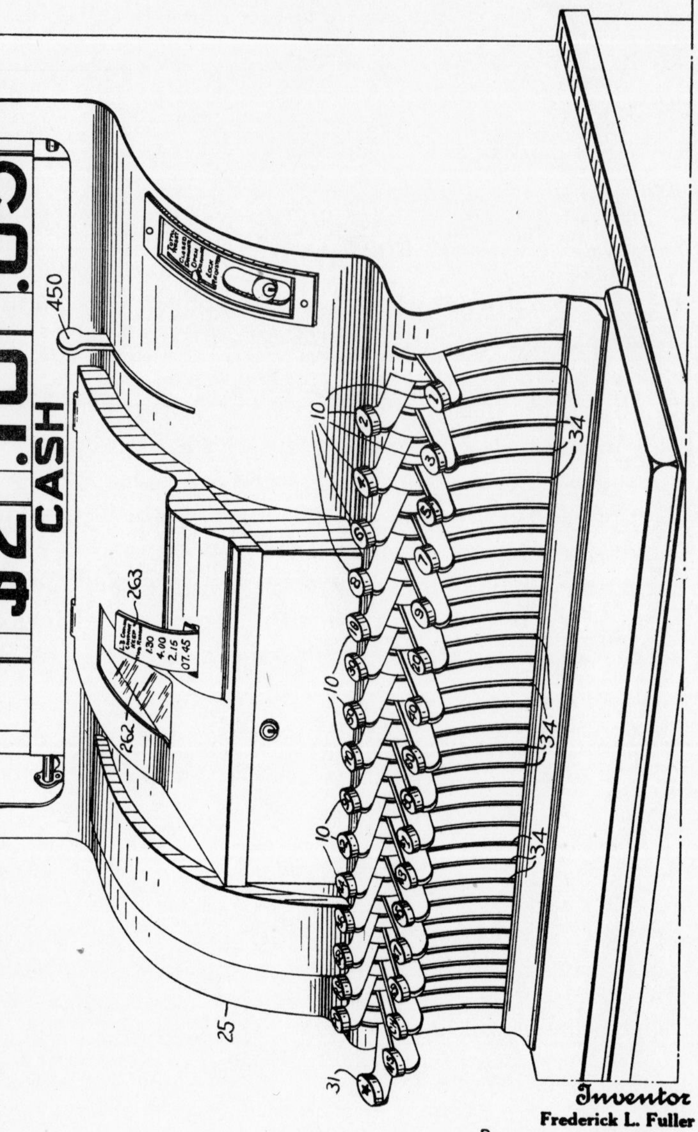

Inventor
Frederick L. Fuller

By Carl Beust

His Attorney

*B*ETTER Cash drawer control was the object of an improvement to cash registers patented by Mr. Fuller on February 9, 1935. The application for this patent said in part:

One object of the present invention is the provision of suitable mechanism to insure the proper control of the cash drawer in coordination with the other functions performed by the machine.

With this and incidental objects in view the invention consists in certain novel features of construction and combination of parts, the essential elements of which are set forth in the appended claims, and a preferred form of embodiment of which is hereinafter described with reference to the drawings which accompany and form part of this specification.

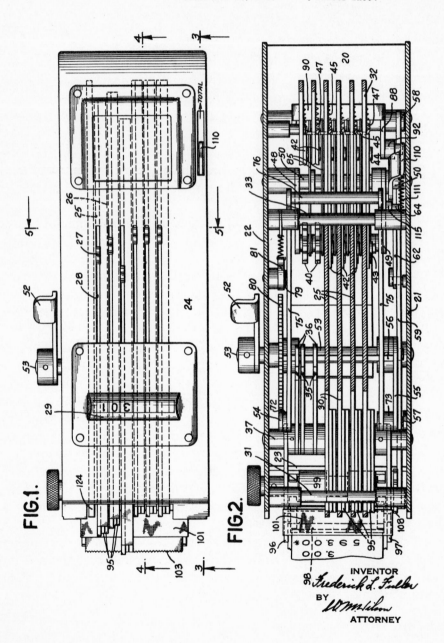

FIG.1.

FIG.2.

INVENTOR
Frederick L. Fuller
BY
L. W. Wilson
ATTORNEY

SIMPLIFICATION of accounting machines in a manner that would eliminate much mechanism and thereby reduce the cost of manufacturing and servicing, was the object of the patent obtained by Mr. Fuller on June 4, 1935. The application descriptive of this improvement said in part:

An object of the invention is to provide a simple item or value entering device comprising manually set indexing devices and co-ordinated total taking mechanism whereby the same indexing devices may also be employed for deriving a total, thus simplifying to a great extent the total taking devices previously used.

Another object of the invention is to provide such indexing devices with type members to provide for both printing the items and the total thereof, since obviously the adjustment of the indexing devices may represent either an item or a total.

A still further object is to provide a manually operable device which establishes a co-operative relationship between the accumulator and the indexing devices whereby the latter may upon adjustment zeroize the accumulator elements and thus secure the total thereon.

A still further object is to characterize a total for identification purposes by providing for the printing of an asterisk alongside of such printed total. A simple construction for providing for the above consists of a special type member which is shifted to printing position by adjustment of the total taking control lever, and is shifted out of printing position after a total printing operation.

Another object of the invention is to simplify the printing mechanisms privided for machines of the type illustrated by requiring fewer parts for effecting an item or total printing impression and feeding the record strip to space successive imprints.

A still further object is to provide a novel and simple form of zero printing mechanism whereby an indexing lever may be set to print a zero by the type but such setting operation will not be transmitted to the related accumulator element.

A still further object of the invention is to provide a suitable operating device in the form of a lever having suitable co-ordinated operated devices whereby various operations can be accomplished by a single manipulation of the lever.

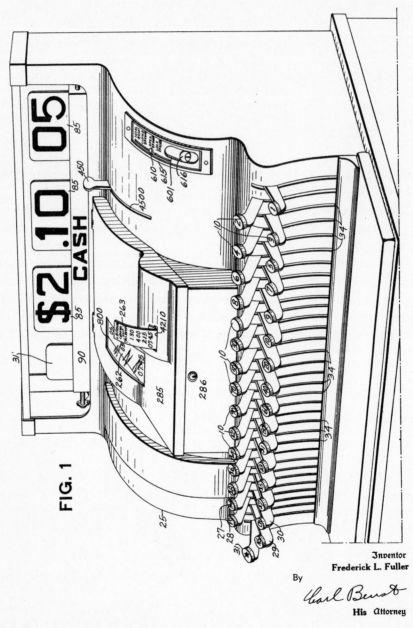

FIG. 1

Inventor

Frederick L. Fuller

By

Carl Benat

His Attorney

ON OCTOBER 1, 1935, there was issued a cash register patent on an application filed February 5, 1932, which said in part:

This invention relates to cash registers or accounting machines and more particularly to that class of machines employing a plurality of accumulators.

The present case is a division of my application for Letters Patents, Serial No. 99,019, filed April 1, 1926, entitled "Cash registers".

One object of the present invention is the provision of suitable mechanism to insure the proper zero setting of the totalizers provided in the machine, and to insure the performance of this function in proper relation to the other functions performed by the machine.

Nov. 5, 1935. F. L. FULLER 2,019,900

ACCOUNTING MACHINE

Original Filed Oct. 21, 1930 5 Sheets-Sheet 1

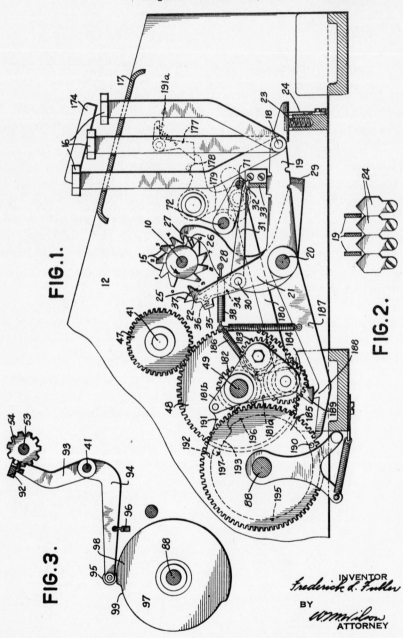

FIG.1.
FIG.2.
FIG.3.

INVENTOR
Frederick L. Fuller
BY
W.M. Wilson
ATTORNEY

*T*HE constant research and experiment on the Proof machine for banks which followed its original construction led Mr. Fuller to apply on February 17, 1934, for a patent which was granted on November 5, 1935. The application for this patent said:

The main object of the present invention is to improve the differential mechanisms under control of the ten keys so as to simplify such mechanisms and cause the operations to be more positive.

In the present construction a source of power is utilized to rotate a master wheel and the latter as it rotates sets up item representing wheels one after the other, such wheels constituting indicating wheels which may be visually read prior to the entry of the item in the accumulator or item printing devices.

In the event of an error the error mechanism, which is also of an improved type, may come into play to reset the item representing wheels so that the item will not be entered in the accumulator or item printing devices, if employed.

A further object of the invention is to improve the error correcting mechanism so that the operation of resetting the item indicating wheels is effected by power and in such manner that such an operation is the only one effected.

The present invention also includes a modification of the error correcting mechanism which is constructed in a different manner but includes the same improved features.

Fig.1

INVENTOR

Frederick L. Fuller

BY

ATTORNEYS

*T*HE cash registers of 1927, due to a number of improvements created and patented by Mr. Fuller in the preceding twenty years, were far superior in every respect. Yet in that year we find him applying for another patent, granted nine years later in 1936, of which his application said:

Cash registers are now upon the market which are adapted to register, print, and indicate the amounts of the successive transactions so that the total of the sales and other related information may be obtained. In some classes of business it is desirable to segregate each transaction into the individual items comprising the transaction so that there will be printed not only the total involved in the transaction, but the individual items as well. With such information upon a slip or issued check the operator may readily check back to ascertain whether or not the articles were properly charged and since the addition of the items is mechanically performed, it will eliminate entirely the danger of incorrectly adding the individual items which is an inherent difficulty in systems in which mental addition is employed.

The principal object of this invention is to provide a cash register with an improved mechanism for recording items and the total of the items either upon an issued check or inserted slip and for simultaneously recording the total on a record strip.

A further object is to provide mechanism whereby the items may be entered in the totalizing devices by merely depressing the operating keys and to provide a separate operating means to record the amounts shown on the totalizer, the recording of which is controlled by the position of the elements of the totalizer.

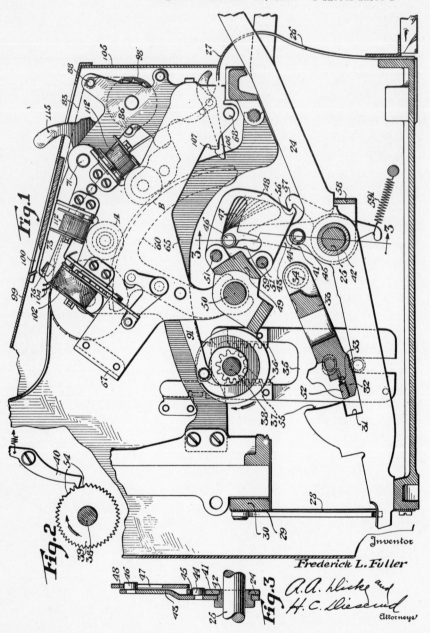

Fig.1

Fig.2

Fig.3

Inventor

Frederick L. Fuller

A. A. Hlicke and
H. C. Diescud
Attorneys

ON DECEMBER 1, 1936, a patent was issued on a cash register application filed February 9, 1933, which said:

The principal object of this invention is to provide an improved differential mechanism which may be utilized for the purpose of adjusting type carriers and indicators as well as actuating accounting machines. In machines of the type used herein for the purpose of illustration it is considered advantageous and desirable, if not altogether necessary, to provide means whereby the keys during their initial movement may be operated independently of the differential mechanisms. This idle movement is particularly important since it permits other mechanisms to be actuated prior to any registering movement of the differential devices and the time which it allows may be employed for a number of purposes, among which may be stated: the latching of the desired keys to the key coupler, the unlocking of the differential actuators, the engagement of a totalizer with the actuators, etc. Moreover, in respect to the printing functions of the machine, it is desirable that the adjusted type carriers be retained in their differentially adjusted positions when the keys have completed their downward strokes so that printing may be properly effected at this time.

TEN-KEY ADDING MACHINE

Original Filed Sept. 7, 1934 5 Sheets-Sheet 1

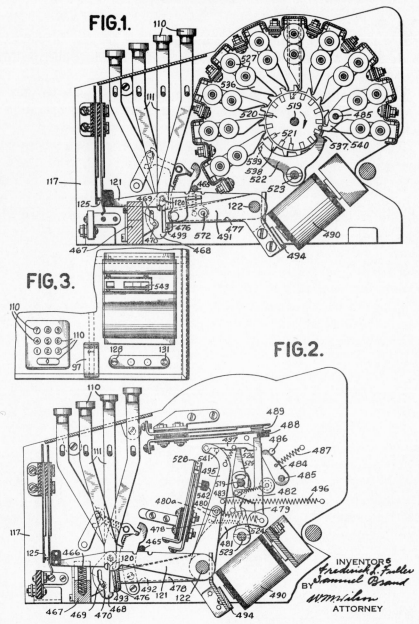

FIG.1.

FIG. 3.

FIG.2.

INVENTORS
Frederick L. Fuller
Samuel Brand
BY
W. M. Wilson
ATTORNEY

*A*N IMPROVED ten key adding machine for use in connection with the Proof Machine for banks was patented by Mr. Fuller on March 16, 1937. The application said:

The main object of the present invention is to devise a ten-key adding machine which is simple in construction, reliable in operation and which requires a minimum of expenditure of manual power.

The present machine is provided with a series of item set-up wheels which are successively set up as the keys are operated. By means of a power-operated mechanism the differential set-up of these wheels is conveyed to a set of printing elements or to totalizer elements. With the exception of the specific form of mechanism herein employed this form of mechanism is old and well known in the art. The present machine includes particularly improved constructions whereby the set-up wheels are successively set up as the keys are operated in a manner that requires a minimum expenditure of manual power.

The item wheels are successively set up by means of a master wheel which is operated by a power drive through a friction drive, the source of power being preferably the same power drive that causes the differential setting of the totalizer or printing elements.

The differential position of the master wheel is controlled by a digit set-up mechanism which consists of a rotary drum provided with a series of longitudinally shiftable pins or digit stops, one of which is in shifted position to normally prevent rotation of the master wheel by the friction drive.

The selection of and the positive shifting of these digit stops are effected by electrical means under control of the keys, the depression of a key causing the energization of a related magnet which shifts the associated digit stop.

FIG.1.

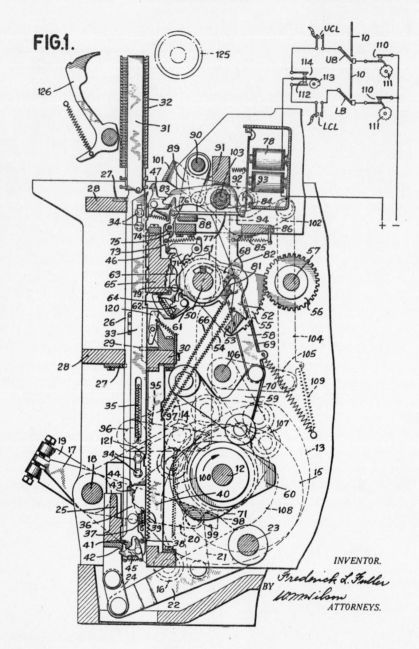

INVENTOR.

Frederick L. Fuller

BY *W. M. Wilson*

ATTORNEYS.

*A*N IMPROVEMENT to the International Alphabetic Accounting and Bookkeeping machine, designed to improve the printing mechanism, was patented on April 13, 1937. In his application for this patent Mr. Fuller said:

One object of the invention is to provide an improved printing mechanism for printing alphabetical as well as numerical characters in which the type characters are moved and locked into printing position in a positive manner. In carrying out this invention there is provided a type carrying member carrying type elements arranged in four groups. One group comprising all of the numerical characters and each of the other groups comprising substantially 1/3 of the alphabetical characters for each group. Each group of alphabet type is represented on a Hollerith record card by perforations in what is known as a zoning position and the numerical type are represented by single perforations in the usual manner. The analyzing stations consist of the usual upper and lower sets of brushes generally used in the well known form of Hollerith tabulating machines and as the record cards pass the upper set of analyzing brushes the zoning perforations are sensed causing a mechanical set to be made in the machine and as the record card passes the lower brushes the numerical perforations are sensed which causes a positive advance in the type bar to select a numeral type or a type adjacent to the corresponding numeral type according to the mechanical setup of machine parts made by the sensing of the zone perforations.

A further object of the invention is to provide a single magnetic tripping means responsive from both upper and lower brushes for initiating both the zoning operation and the type selecting operation.

A still further object of the invention is to provide means for shifting the circuit of the magnetic tripping means from the upper to the lower set of brushes during each card cycle.

FIG.1.

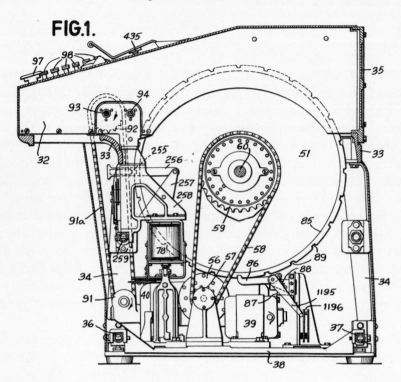

FIG.2.

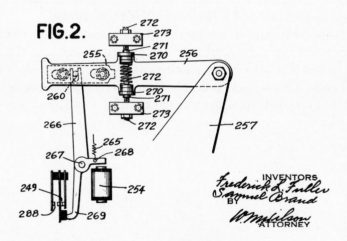

INVENTORS
Frederick L. Fuller
Samuel Brand
BY
W. M. Wilson
ATTORNEY

CONTROL of the speed of the sorting drum of the Proof machine for banks was improved by an invention patented by Mr. Fuller and Samuel Brand on May 4, 1937. The application for this patent said:

Prior to the present invention check sorting machines of the manually-controlled type have been designed and constructed to cause the drum carrying sorting compartments to be rotated in the shorter of two directions to select a compartment by a minimum movement of the drum. The speed of rotation of the drum gradually increased as its inertia was overcome and it was especially noted that whenever the drum rotated through its longest arcuate movements the high speed of the drum was detrimental to the machine when the drum was stopped at the desired position by obstructing its rotation. In the present construction a maximum torque is initially applied to quickly rotate the drum but by the provision of suitable braking devices the speed of the drum is gradually reduced, facilitating its stopping.

The main object of the invention is, therefore, the provision of improvements to change the speed of rotation of the drum. In the present arrangement this is effected by a reversal of the motor current to cause dynamic braking and also by the provision of an electrical resistance in the motor circuit and a mechanical friction brake.

The reversal of current and the insertion of electrical resistance takes place irrespective of the direction of rotation of the electrical motor and when the drum approaches its desired position. The mechanical brake also functions to hold the drum in its desired position of adjustment but it is released upon the depression of a subsequent key.